A Tractor In The House

& Other Smashing Farm Stories

Joe Peck

To Roger –
Merry Christmas 2005
Enjoy!
Joe Peck

Also by Joe Peck

A Cow In The Pool
& Udder Humorous Farm Stories

A Tractor in the House

& Other Smashing Farm Stories

Joe Peck

Illustrations by Joe Craig

Peckhaven Publishing
178 Wagman's Ridge
Saratoga Springs NY 12866
2005

A Tractor in the House
& Other Smashing Farm Stories

By Joe Peck
Illustrations by Joe Craig

Published by:
Peckhaven Publishing
178 Wagman's Ridge
Saratoga Springs NY 12866-6620
www.joepeckonline.com
e-mail: joe@joepeckonline.com

International Standard Book Number: 978-0-9714620-3-8

Library of Congress Control Number: 2005908252

First Edition
Printed in the United States of America

INTRODUCTION

This book is a celebration of all the vitality, excitement and humor found on a family dairy farm. Its stories attempt to give the reader a unique and lighthearted look at everyday farm life and reflect my innate optimism no matter what happens. There isn't room for pessimism on a busy farm. After a lifetime of farming I have learned how important a positive attitude and a sense of humor are to the farm and family's success.

The unsung heroine of this book is my wonderful wife, Pat, whose tireless efforts at typing, compiling and prodding me have brought this book to reality. Special thanks to our son and farm partner, David, who let me take the time to write, to our daughter Deborah and husband Sean for work on the website and story ideas, and to our youngest child, Sharon, for her valuable help in revising and injecting a refreshing twist into many of the stories.

For their endorsements, I thank Carolyn Zielinski, a farm wife from far off Oregon for her encouraging words; John Vogel, American Agriculturalist editor, for his vision and inspiration; and Nate Rudgers, NYS Ag Commissioner, for his support as a friend and his positive attitude as a spokesperson for agriculture everywhere. For the cover and wonderful drawings, I am grateful to Joe Craig, a family friend with a talent for catching the true essence of a situation in his caricatures. Thanks also to Rich Romano, a fellow Toastmaster and author, for his assistance with computer software use and cover design.

I must acknowledge the inspiration and sense of humor I got from my Aunt Milly Haas Shaw, whose wonderful positive attitude has kept our entire family going. And a special thanks to all the farmers, farm wives, agribusiness people and so many others who have, in one way or another, contributed to the stories in this book.

A sense of humor is such a valuable possession. It takes the cry out of a crisis. It makes a cow in the pool or a tractor in the house a problem to solve rather than a disaster. Take a moment from your stressful life, read these stories, and soon you will see the humor in your life.

ABOUT THE AUTHOR

Joe Peck, a Cornell University graduate, Advanced Toastmaster, and humorous speaker, milks 100 registered Holsteins on Peckhaven Farm in Saratoga County, NY, in partnership with his son David. The farm is both a Century Farm and Dairy of Distinction.

An agricultural leader, Joe has been recognized by Cornell University as an outstanding alumnus and by the governor of New York for the contributions that he and his family have made to agriculture and their community.

Joe's optimism, sense of humor, and farm experience helped him become a popular speaker, storyteller and accomplished writer of humorous farm stories which have appeared in numerous publications. He is author of *A Cow In The Pool & Udder Humorous Farm Stories.*

A member of the National Speakers Association and Toastmasters, Joe has been entertaining farm audiences for years with a combination of enlightened inspiration, homespun yarns and stand-up comedy, drawn from a lifetime of farm experience.

Joe uses good, clean family-style humor, lives up to his reputation for being funny, and sends people out on a high note, feeling good about themselves.

FOR SCHEDULING INFORMATION:
Joe Peck
Peckhaven Farm
178 Wagman's Ridge
Saratoga Springs NY 12866
(518) 584-4129
joe@joepeckonline.com

CONTENTS

Chapter 1   **Country Living**

Ten Tips for New Country Dwellers   13

How To Pass A Tractor   15

Driving By A Farm   17

Clues   19

Family Style Dinners   21

Garage Sales   23

Watching   25

If Farmers Had Garage Sales   27

Watching The County Road   29

Maize Mazes   31

What Is A Dairy Princess?   33

Another Country   35

Bidders Beware   37

How To Paint A Barn   39

Chapter 2   **Is Farming An Art?**

Is Farming An Art?   43

I Am A Farmer   45

Stingy or Tight   47

Beware of Ear Piercing Noise   49

Dozing Off   51

White Pants   53

Types of Farmers   55

Your Farm From The Air   57

Things A Farmer Will Not Do   59

My Big Moment   61

Exercise   63

Farm Programs On Line   65

Parlor Perspectives   67

Why Farmers Make Good Husbands   69

Why Farmers Farm   71

Wedding Vows for Farmers   73

Your Must Live On A Dairy Farm If   75

Chapter 3   **Farm Lessons**

What They Should Teach You In Ag School	77
Mystery Solving	79
Multi-Tasking	81
Differences	83
Optimists and Pessimists	85
Changed Environment	87
My 'To Do' Lists	89
Fastidious Faces	91
Personality Profiles	93
Farm Friendly Olympics	95
Manure Musings	97
Avoiding Boredom	99
Stuck In A Rut	101

Chapter 4   **Cow Curiosities**

Bobbling Bottles	103
Calves As Pets	105
Life With Cows	107
Frolicking Calves	109
Advice Column For Cows	111
Cow Tips	113
Career Cows	115
Maps	117
Do Cows Talk?	119
Smart Cows	121
The Cow As A Food Processor	123
Cow Etiquette	125
Do Cows Ever Sleep?	127
Athletic Trainers	129
Bovine Ballet Steps	131

Chapter 5   **Helping Hands**

Milk Haulers   135

Sales People   137

Recycling   139

The Job Interview   141

Ode To A Tractor   143

Personal Ad   147

My Milk Truck Drivers   149

Overheard In The Barn   151

Working On A Farm   153

Becoming Computer Literate   155

Chapter 6   **Magical Machines**

Shut Down   157

What Is Auto Steering   159

Emergency Call   161

Battling Hedgerows   163

Footbaths   165

Hammers   167

Plowing   169

Great Adventure   171

The Scoop On Skid Steers   173

Electricity   175

My New Smerff   177

Chapter 7   **Weather Woes**

How To Survive Winter   179
The Blizzard of '93   181
Christmas Day   183
Christmas In The One-Room School   185
Fooling The Cows   187
Spring Is Coming   189
The Twelve Days Of Christmas
   On The Farm   191
Numbers   193
A Christmas Story   195
Cold Snap   197

Chapter 8   **Reminiscences**

What Do You Make?   199
Evening Chores   201
Priceless   203
Change   205
Recycled Barns   207
History Lesson   209
It Could Happen To Anybody   211
Stages of Life   213
If Only I Had Time   215
The Earth Is Shrinking   217
That's Where I Came In   219
A Christmas To Remember   221

Chapter 1

TEN TIPS FOR NEW COUNTRY DWELLERS

1. Try to straddle unidentified objects in the road. They may look like mud but they probably are not.

2. Don't pick and take home and cook any of those big juicy ears of corn growing near the road. Trust me, it is NOT sweet corn.

3. You may visit my farm, and even bring your guests with you. Please call ahead, for you see, I might be talking to my cows and you may not understand some of the words I am using.

4. What you smell as you pass my farm is not an odor, but rather the perfume of the producers of nature's most perfect food.

5. When meeting a farm truck, tractor or self-propelled farm machine on a narrow road, allow them plenty of room to pass because, while they mean you no harm, they are bigger than you are.

6. Do not attempt to pass a slow moving farm machine unless you are really, really in a hurry, and you know that no one is coming the other way, and also know that the farmer realizes that you are behind him.

7. What is spraying out of the back of those large tanks we pull through the fields is NOT irrigation water.

8. Those little plastic houses our calves spend the first month of their lives in are called "hutches" for the man who invented them in 1961, Rudolf Hutch.

9. Those large open green areas are really fields used for growing a hay crop to feed to our cows. These fields are not to be used for doing wheelies with 4-wheel drive vehicles. Any vehicles caught tearing up my fields will be confiscated, but only if they have automatic transmission and air conditioning.

10. Those large open-ended cellars that seem to be full to the top of the walls for over half their length are called bunker silos. They serve the same purpose – storing ensiled forage for the cows - as the big tall round ones. They are square because they tend to flatten out when we lay them down.

I hope that these brief explanations of some of the sights you see as you drive by a dairy farm on your daily commute to your dull and boring non-farm job, help you better understand and appreciate the interesting and exciting world of your farmer neighbor.

HOW TO PASS A TRACTOR

As farm sizes grow and fields are farther and farther apart, encountering a slow tractor on a narrow road is a growing problem. Often when I'm heading to or from the fields I notice an impatient driver dying to get around me. The guy tailgating me in the SUV may not realize how much dexterity it takes to keep a tractor on only one half of the road. He also may not understand that tractors weren't built for highway speeds. In fact, eighteen miles an hour on a tractor is really fast.

So, how does one pass a tractor? Well, it depends on how much of a hurry you are in, how far you think the tractor is going and how much risk are you willing to take. Most country roads were not designed with long straight stretches for cars to pass slow-moving farm machinery. In addition, if you follow a tractor long enough, you will begin to see how hard it is to drive big machines in a straight line.

This proclivity for wandering all over both sides of the road is exacerbated by accumulated wear in the tractor's steering mechanism. And, to be fair, this erratic driving may have something do to with the fact that the driver may be attempting to eat his peanut butter and jelly sandwich and drink a cup of hot coffee, while bringing a full load of silage back to the farm.

If you are lucky, the wandering farm vehicle ahead of you will veer back onto its own side of the road at the exact instant that the road becomes devoid of any oncoming traffic, allowing you to pass. Of course, this opportunity is only apt to happen once a decade. Before attempting this maneuver, you must get a feel for whether the tractor driver realizes that someone is following him. Ask yourself if there is evidence of a rear-view mirror on the tractor, or whether the driver occasionally turns around for a quick glance behind him.

If the answer to both of these questions is no, don't attempt to zip by the rig ahead of you. There is no greater sinking feeling than to try to overtake a tractor on a narrow road when the huge machine inevitably starts to veer into the opposite lane. At that point you only have two choices: speed up or slow down. Whether you have confidence enough to pass a tractor really depends on whether your wife is in the front or the back seat.

If you don't make it by, it might be a signal for you to slow down and relax. Enjoy the scenery and take in all of the open spaces that farmers have preserved for you. This would be an excellent opportunity to reflect on how you might leave a little earlier next time.

DRIVING BY A FARM

When someone in the business world seeks to learn more by visiting others in their field it is called professional development. As for my professional development, I like to explore back country roads on the chance that I will pass an active farm and learn something new that I can use in my own operation. And my wife thinks I am just lost and won't admit it!

Studying farm operations from the road is an exact science that requires keen observational skills combined with the ability to drive slowly enough to view all you want to see. However, be careful not to go so slowly that you draw attention to yourself or you might be mistaken for a bill collector, milk inspector, or worse yet, the town assessor.

Unfortunately, many farms are no longer in business. Yet the buildings remain as grim reminders of where an active farm family once cared for the land and animals for a century or more before succumbing to the lure of shorter hours, a higher standard of living, and the opportunity to sleep late once in a while.

The first clue to whether a farmstead is still the home of commercial animals of any kind is the presence of mud. No farm can exist for long without signs of ankle deep mud in areas approaching the barns. A fenced-in barnyard green with grass and weeds is enough to know this farm hasn't been home to large animals for some time. Also, the more mud there is in the road by a farm, the greater chance the farm is still active.

Another sign is the numbers and placement of machines around the farmstead. A farm may look great for a color portrait on a calendar with nothing but red barns, white board fences and green lawn-like yards, but a real farm has tractors, miscellaneous machines and calf hutches scattered all over the yard, driveways and even the road.

But the most important way to confirm a farm's fate is to look for signs of its owner doing things a farmer would never have time to do. Are the fences made of freshly painted white boards enclosing a weed-free lawn? Are there flower boxes under the milk house windows? Is there a flagpole in the center of the barnyard surrounded by a bed of mulched perennials within a tractor tire painted white? If so, these are sure signs of someone having too much leisure time.

So as you explore back country roads, beware of slow moving vehicles for they might be driven by farmers engaged in professional development.

CLUES

Sherlock Holmes, the world famous fictional detective, is renowned for his remarkable powers of observation and deduction. Few readers realize that this ability to piece together seemingly random clues into an iron-clad case is the result of author Sir Arthur Conan Doyle's training as a physician. He was taught to use every possible detail about his patient, both observed and deduced, to make an accurate diagnosis.

These same powers can be used to tell if someone you have just met grew up on a farm. Many farm-raised youth will, upon maturation, try to shed the airs of a 'country kid'. Fortunately, no matter how much they try to become sophisticated and citified, farm kids will always betray their rural upbringing with a series of clues, detectable only by the most observant.

Anyone who vigorously wipes his or her feet on the mat, then enters your house through the back door was undoubtedly raised on a farm. Likewise, those who know what all those logos on caps actually stand for or have a compulsion to hoard used baler twine probably grew up on a farm.

Your suspect was raised on a farm if he says things like, "You don't need to buy a new hose. Just wrap the hole with duct tape and it will last a long time," or, "Oh, that's all right, a few spatters of mud on my new khakis won't hurt anything."

Another clue that reveals a person's rural upbringing is something as simple as where they park their car. Sometimes visitors to my farm leave their cars in the middle of the yard, as if the place were as devoid of activity as an abandoned rail yard. Any farm-raised person knows that the average farm yard witnesses a continuous flow of people, tractors, trucks and assorted animals, so it is important to park as far out of the way as possible, and never in front of the milk house or generator house.

How one manages time is another indication of a person's early training. An obvious sign of one's coming from a farm family is how fast he eats. A person who can consume a bountiful, slaved-over, home-cooked, lip-smacking good meal in less than six minutes, including dessert, probably came from a large farm family. If someone gets edgy around chore time or feels guilty about taking time off during good weather, they may simply be the product of a farm background.

But the best way to determine if your suspect came from a farm is to observe intently the anguished look on his face when you mention the joys and virtues of such jobs as walking through the brambles in a 20 acre pasture in search of a newborn calf, loading baled hay on a blistering hot day or picking rock any time.

FAMILY STYLE DINNERS

I love family style dinners, the kind served in Grange halls and church basements. Everyone gets more than enough to eat and there always seems to be plenty of food left over.

The best dinners require sitting at long narrow tables where everyone is squeezed together, literally elbow-to-elbow. Because people are seated in the order that they arrive, these dinners afford an excellent opportunity to meet new people. But the best part is the food, all served family style. I don't know why this style is called family style. My family never eats like this.

The kitchen crew brings large platters of meat, followed by massive bowls of mashed potatoes and vegetables and pitchers of gravy. It seems like I always sit one place beyond where the mashed potatoes run out. Not to worry though as someone from the kitchen crew will swoop up the empty bowl and return shortly with another one, piled high with more steaming spuds. I just worry about frail old ladies carrying heavy platters or eight-year old boys pouring hot coffee. Fortunately, I haven't witnessed any kitchen catastrophes.

At most family style dinners there is no shortage of food, especially desserts. I relish the opportunity to search the dessert table for such local specialties as apple dumplings, rhubarb cobbler or chocolate éclairs, in addition to the usual variety of homemade pies, cakes and chocolate chip cookies. I shy away from anything I can't identify. I know that I am supposed to take only one dessert, but I always explain that I am taking the second one to someone else. That way I get a second dessert and the dessert table guard thinks that I am a very thoughtful person.

The old adage "take all you can eat, but eat all you take" applies here. At a recent roast pork dinner in a crowded church hall I witnessed a shocking breach of etiquette that I will not soon forget. The small, slender lady on my left, whom I had just met, seemed to be enjoying her meal and had helped herself to a more than ample portion of sliced roast pork. Nothing was wrong with that, for so had I. When I was finished I felt stuffed and certain that I wouldn't need any breakfast the next day. However, when I glanced to my left I caught this otherwise nice lady sliding several slices of roast pork into a small resealable plastic bag that she had removed from her purse. It was obvious to all that she had enough meat for her lunch and dinner the next day. I was astonished! Should I report her to the kitchen crew or at least point out how selfish an act she was performing? After all, if everyone took a serving home with them, a few more pigs would be needed.

Yes, I love family style dinners, but I'll never bring a plastic bag to one.

GARAGE SALES

Spring means the return of warm weather, green grass and, thankfully, garage sales. This wonderful American institution adds meaning and purpose to human life, especially after a too long winter.

My garage sale strategy consists of carefully analyzing all of the classified ads on Thursdays in order to plan my route for the following Saturday morning. I search for those sales that appear worth visiting, especially the ones in upscale neighborhoods where folks think nothing of throwing away last year's clothes, televisions and toboggans. Ruled out are those featuring baby clothes, exercise equipment, and china of any kind. I only circle those mentioning masculine things like ladders, hand tools, chain saws and computer printers or ones proclaiming 'moving south– everything must go'.

I love garage sales. I love rummaging through piles of long silent alarm clocks, headless electric razors, clock radios that still talk but no longer tell time and battery chargers that have been run over, all in the hope of finding one priceless treasure, like an almost new hammer drill, still in its box, or a desk swivel chair without protruding springs, all shamelessly under priced.

I love searching through items tagged with labels of as many different colors as there are neighbors who contribute to this friendly social event. My only complaint is that too often the signs directing one to a garage sale are left up long after the sale is over, left to the ravages of nature to render them faceless.

I hope I'm not too picky, but my advice to choice garage sale holders is to please take these signs down after your event is officially over. As you put away the things that did not sell, the mismatched Tupperware, the dull hedge clippers and the pail of broken plumbing fixtures, ask the kids to remove the sign leaning against the old stump out front and the ones at the intersection directing folks to your sale. Tell them all of this must be done before the whole family can head for McDonalds to spend your weekend's earnings.

If these signs are removed promptly, my faint heart will no longer skip a beat when I see a garage sale sign on a foggy Tuesday morning, only to find a forlorn garage, its mouth closed in tight silence. To me there is nothing worse than a missed garage sale.

WATCHING

While visiting with an avid bird watcher recently I was amazed to learn how much we have in common. For example, he was bragging about the rare and exotic birds he has seen in his travels to the native habitats of many avian species. In fact, as with many 'birders', he keeps a list of all the birds he has ever seen. How interesting, I thought. I keep just a list myself. Only my list is of rare and exotic farm tractors.

You see, I am a confirmed and addicted tractor watcher and, as with birdwatchers, I, too, travel to exotic places in hopes of spotting a not-often-seen example of early rural Americana. Tractor seeking has many advantages over birdwatching. First, you don't have to sneak up on them in small boats. And you don't need field glasses to study them. Thirdly, you can examine them up close without fear of bite or flight.

Surprisingly enough I experience the same exhilaration upon spotting a rare tractor that a birdwatcher does upon sighting an uncommon bird. I'll never forget the first time I saw that rare Steel-Wheeled Low-Bellied Mud Sticker sitting there in all its glory. It was a real pleasure to add that one to my list.

Rare tractors are harder to find than rare birds. Oh, I know there are always museums, tractor shows, thresher reunions, county fairs and private collections to search through, but the truly hard to find ones are usually too valuable to be readily available to the public. This means that the thrill of the hunt drives us to seek out our quarry.

So far I have added to my list the Bark-Shinned Narrow Fendered Furrow Hopper, the Red-Radiatored Smoke Belcher and the much sought after Green Flywheeled Ear Popper. But, alas, despite my years of searching, I've yet to spot the rarest tractor of all. Yes, I am talking about the Orange Pileated Steel-Seated Hernia-Maker. But, like any true bird watcher, I shall never give up the search.

IF FARMERS HAD GARAGE SALES

It's a sad fact of life that the only thing that holds our whole fragile economy together is garage sales. Without their ability to keep large volumes of currency in a constant state of exchange, we might be faced with another great depression.

Always one to do my part to keep the economy strong, I stop at as many garage sales as I can squeeze into each weekend. However, all I ever find are typical household items like dishes, toys and electronic gadgets. What I really need is a garage sale for farmers where nearly new farm items can be purchased for bargain prices.

I began looking around our farmstead for all the no-longer-needed items that I could sell in my first annual garage sale for farmers. I unearthed all kinds of treasures. I found a short stack of white plastic pails firmly stuck together, several cans of paint in a range of colors, all with less than one inch of paint in them, half a bag of five-year-old seed corn of assorted varieties, and a box of instruction books for machines we no longer own.

Next I discovered two shovels with broken handles, an old horse collar with its straw stuffing protruding through the many holes which mice had chewed in it, one tractor chain made mostly of repair links, two aerosol cans of fly spray that had lost their fizz, and three torn Tingley boots, all for the left foot.

Collecting all these priceless objects was spurred on by visions of the money I would make. I added to my pile an old piston water pump with a cracked housing, a miracle knife-sharpener (as seen on television, the only place it actually worked), a box of used milker inflations, one half bag of bent nails, a roll of garden hose with two splices and a fitting on only one end, and a ladder with two broken rungs. Then I uncovered a stack of bushel baskets without bottoms, two milk cans without tops, a pile of 2x4's too short to use, a box of snaps with broken springs, and a bladeless jackknife.

As I searched it struck me that the reason farmers don't have garage sales is because they save everything. They cannot bring themselves to part with anything. Worse yet, they keep going to garage sales and bringing home even more junk. I don't know about everybody else, but I only save what is not worth keeping, yet too good to throw away. I am happy to do my part. After all, you never know when we might have another depression.

WATCHING THE COUNTY ROAD

Since we live on a back road with light, almost boring traffic, I always look forward to working the few fields we have bordering the county road. That's where the action is! All day long cars and trucks stream by whizzing their way to unknown destinations. I can relieve my boredom by guessing where the ready mix truck is going or who will be getting that load of lumber.

This spring I saw a sight that still intrigues me. I was mowing first cutting and had just finished my mid-morning banana, when a bicyclist loomed around the corner, dressed in the prerequisite spandex suit and fingerless riding gloves, wearing an obviously expensive helmet, and pedaling rhythmically at a steady pace. So far this was not an unusual sight.

Here comes the unusual part! Following the biker was a white windowless van with a photographer sitting sidesaddle on its roof. The van carried the logo of a prominent bike manufacturer. My clever mind quickly deduced that this was a photo shoot for a company promotional brochure. The van top perch was a perfect spot to get unobstructed shots of a happy biker cruising along beautiful country roads.

Apparently the last time the bike company put a cameraman on top of a van he must have fallen off because this guy was securely tethered to a big screw eye bolted to the roof of the van.

What a great way to get a snapshot from a new perspective. I envision photographers delicately balanced on dump wagons to get that unforgettable shot of a forage harvester or perched in a hedgerow tree clicking away at a new model tractor bearing down on them. The opportunities are endless.

I expect to see hordes of farm-oriented shutterbugs climbing silos, lying on their backs aiming at curious cows and poking their heads through barn windows, all to get that one priceless shot that they hope will bring them fame and fortune.

But enough fantasizing about photographers swarming all over my farm. What I should do is find a way to make public relations people pay me for providing such a picturesque setting for their shots. After all, if it weren't for farmers' rolling green fields, the background in all those photos would be brown weeds, bland forests or treeless housing developments.In retrospect, I'm just glad that I had my cleaner tee shirt on today, the one with only three holes and an oil stain, just in case I made it into the shot.

MAIZE MAZES

I am amazed at the interest everyone has in corn mazes. After all, they are nothing but a confusing network of inter-connecting paths whose outlet is hard to find. Sounds like my last trip to the mall.

I've thought about capitalizing on this latest agri-tourism phenomenon, but I am too lazy to do it right. Most people don't realize how difficult it is to create a first rate corn maze. It's not just a matter of planting a field of corn, waiting a few weeks for the plants to emerge and snipping off an occasional stalk to form a random pattern of paths. Nothing is that easy. First, you have to pay some expert to design a complicated pattern that has to be painstakingly super-imposed on a huge cornfield. Impossible, you say. Well, it would be for me.

I have always prided myself on finding the easiest and cheapest way to accomplish my goals. With this in mind, I am proposing a quick, painless, and economical way to turn any field of nearly mature corn into an almost first rate corn maze.

All you have to do is turn a cow loose in the tall corn and let her thrash around for a suitable length of time. She will make many twists and turns, seeking a way out. When you feel enough paths have been trampled down, simply park the mixer wagon near where you want the maze to end. If she hasn't been fed for a while she will emerge from the tasseled field and follow the feed wagon right into the barn. It works every time, smooth as silk.

It is important that this method employ only one cow. More would be overkill, resulting in too many paths and not enough stalks left standing. I have never actually tried this approach but a lifetime of experience chasing cows from cornfields makes me think this method would work.

In order to make a trip to my corn maze an all day affair, additional games such as pumpkin toss, cob carving, and hide the zucchini are being developed. That's the kernel of my idea, but it will probably never germinate.

WHAT IS A DAIRY PRINCESS?

A dairy princess is a starry-eyed teenager, more at home feeding a newborn calf than speaking at a Farm Bureau annual meeting. She is a tomboy in sneakers, sweatshirt and jeans who has been told by the County Dairy Princess Committee that being a dairy princess is really easy and a lot of fun. They tell her she should have no problem carrying a full academic program in school, being a cheerleader, feeding calves daily and meeting the requirements of a dairy princess. In spite of her concern about taking on too much, she reluctantly agrees to give it a try.

The big night comes and this future emissary for dairy farmers, in her white gown, manages an almost graceful walk up the aisle, a creditable speech and then tears of joy during the winning announcement and ensuing coronation.

Her family beams with pride, little knowing the thousands of miles they will travel during the coming year so that she can spread the word about our wonderful dairy products.

A dairy princess is really a courageous teenager thrown into the difficult field of public relations. She must enchant first graders with a visit from a real dairy princess, convince dairy farmers that all of her hard work does result in more milk consumed and, above all, she must always appear to consumers to love all dairy products and be happy that she has a role in promoting their use.

This tireless worker may be found making a thirty second radio spot, promoting cheese, handing out yogurt samples by a supermarket dairy case or sitting on the back of a horse-drawn wagon in a local parade. It is all in a day's work for these unsung heroines of milk promotion.

As the next dairy princess banquet approaches, she has mixed emotions. On the one hand she is having a hard time keeping up her hectic pace, but on the other hand she will miss the wonderful time she is having.

Again, the big night finally comes, she sadly crowns her successor and, as she makes her farewell speech, we all stare spellbound at this once tongue-tied, unsure kid. She has, in one year's time, become a well-spoken, self-assured and graceful young lady whose confidence in herself and her future fills the room.

Yes, that is what a dairy princess is. We dairy farmers are proud of them all and are eternally grateful for all the hard work and sacrifice they and their families have made to promote our product.

ANOTHER COUNTRY

As more suburbanites move to the country they seem to find it hard to understand how farmers think. That's because being raised on a farm is very much like being raised in another country. Farmers do have different traditions, languages, and philosophies of life.

Take our view of leisure time, for example. Most new neighbors look upon their leisure time as a God given right, an entitlement allowing them to choose from a menu of acceptable, status-conscious activities, all in the name of 'relaxing' from the demands of their job and stressful commute.

Farmers, on the other hand, are so driven to get everything done before tomorrow, when it starts all over again, that they look upon leisure activities with fear, dread and even guilt. They know that time spent playing golf or skiing is time that could be better spent splitting wood or greasing manure spreaders. Fashionable yuppie neighbors look upon hiking as an opportunity to get some aerobic exercise while communing with nature. We farmers find it hard to imagine anyone choosing to walk several miles through snake and mosquito infested woods and not even search for a lost calf.

Because a farmer's life is, out of necessity, one of constant activity, it is very difficult for him, at the end of a busy day, to have sufficient energy and enthusiasm to pursue and enjoy typical leisure activities without falling asleep. This explains why you may find a farmer dozing in a movie theater, in his pew at church or in the stands at a demolition derby.

The plain truth is, farmers would rather sharpen an ax than go cross country skiing, dehorn a calf than play golf, and repair a roller door than attempt white water canoeing. There is one activity, however, that all of us who live in the country have in common, and that is a commitment to spend as much time as possible with our families. Farmers just choose to spend their precious family time in such bonding activities as stacking wood, feeding calves and painting fences.

Just think of those poor suburbanites who've never enjoyed such experiences as bringing home baby pigs in the back of a station wagon, systematically searching a freshly mown hayfield together looking for a lost log chain, or chasing loose heifers out of the garden clad only in pajamas and bedroom slippers. To others this might seem like living in a foreign country, but to a farm family it's home in America.

BIDDERS BEWARE

You can learn a lot at farm auctions as long as you aren't distracted by what is being sold. Auctions attract all types of lookers and buyers. Here is my guide to determine who might be bidding against you when the action begins.

Most auction crowds are cluttered with retired farmers who have no intention of bidding or buying. They are there to reminisce about how they once had one just like it. Some see it as an opportunity to get out of the house to visit with other retired farmers and generally walk around in the blind hope that someone will ask them for free advice, the one thing they have plenty of. Don't worry about them – they are harmless.

Another character you don't have to worry about is the city slicker. This is someone who may be knowledgeable in his own area of expertise, but since moving to the country, wants to become an expert on all things farm. He may pepper you with questions, but rarely has enough nerve to actually bid on something for fear that he will pay too much for it and be the laughing stock of the farm community.

The expert is easy to spot. He will examine the machine at great length, twisting, shaking and poking into everything he can find to test for wear, breakage, and hidden faults. If this is done with enough confidence and flair, a crowd will gather as the examination continues. An occasional, "Tsk, tsk", "Uh, Oh" and "I thought so" adds to this air of authority. This, too, is to be ignored because he probably doesn't know any more about the condition of the machine than you do.

Also to be ignored are the jokesters. These are two obvious friends who think they are funny making comments as they walk by each machine like, "Wow, has that one been through the mill," or "I feel sorry for whoever buys that one." They won't be bidding either. They just came to the auction for its entertainment value.

The character you do have to watch out for, particularly if there is one farm machine you really want and secretly hope will sell cheap, is the spinner. This is someone who helps you thoroughly analyze the condition of the object in question, pointing out all of its weak points, wear points, and broken points. He will leave you with the feeling, "Wow, I didn't realize it was in such rough shape."

After that, you don't know whether to snap up what you thought was a bargain or to stay away from something with so many things wrong with it. Don't be surprised, when the bidding starts on your desired machine, to find this person bidding against you, topping your every bid. As the other bidders drop out, obviously fearing what they had been told was true, you are even more perplexed.

What a great tactic. The next auction I go to I am going to stand beside the machine I want to buy and spin stories about how worn out it is, how it never worked right when it was new and how anybody would be foolish to bid on it today. Hey, it worked for him. I didn't buy it.

HOW TO PAINT A BARN

I love the look of a freshly painted set of farm buildings, especially when they are "barn" red, trimmed with white. Unfortunately, it is a lot of work and expense to dress up a barn with a fresh coat of paint. In fact, the task may seem so daunting that it usually is put off until either a wedding, family reunion or a visit from the pope warrants a complete spiffing up of your farm buildings.

Now there are many ways to prepare oneself, both physically and mentally, to paint a barn. The most important detail is to be sure the cans of paint are all the same color. Nothing can spoil your day faster than to find that the red is either too red or not red enough or all four cans in a case are not the same shade.

The next most important item you will need is a full can of bee and hornet spray. Trust me, trying to swat mud wasps with a four-inch paintbrush is neither effective, economical or neat. As for the brush, the cheap ones seem to work as well as the premium, super-duper ones and I feel less guilty when I drop one into the sand pile or manure spreader.

At this point I want to clear up one nagging question that I know you are about to ask, which is: "Do you start at the top and work down or start at the bottom and work up?" That all depends on whether or not you are afraid of heights. If climbing tall ladders doesn't bother you, start at the top. If, however, you are afraid to climb anything higher than your head, start at the bottom. That way, if you are lucky, someone will finish the high part for you when they see what a beautiful job you did on the lower half.

If all this sounds too difficult, there is always the possibility someone will come along in a shiny new pickup with out-of-state plates and an unfamiliar accent and offer to spray paint all your buildings for one ridiculously low price. If you do choose this option just remember, not only will the barn be painted, but also all the windows, doors, flowerbeds and even a few slow cats.

Chapter 2

IS FARMING AN ART?

I recently had a long chat with a prominent performing artist who boasted that being a true artist requires discipline, commitment and a belief in the value of the craft. By this definition farmers are really artists, too! It takes more discipline to learn to back a four-wheeled wagon uphill into a shed in the pouring rain than to play the violin, and more commitment to keep your rows absolutely straight when planting corn in the dim light from tractor headlights at 1 a.m. while very drowsy than to pretend to be someone you are not for three whole acts. And more belief in your craft to pull a calf at midnight than to paint a beautiful scene that could have been photographed just as easily.

This performing artist said that to learn an art requires the integration of several different areas of expertise and that good art is not performed in isolation, but rather requires many unseen partners, an ensemble, if you will. That sounds just like farming. I couldn't farm without the cooperation of suppliers, veterinarians, consultants and a loyal and well-trained staff, plus a wife willing to tell me when I'm wrong. Each contributes to my success, just as a performer's perfect solo results from the efforts of those who have helped him perfect his art.

I also learned that impulse plays an important role in learning one's art. Impulse is defined as being aware of what others are doing and will do, and responding naturally to these actions. This probably means trusting your own intuition. It also explains how musicians know when to take a deep breath. That's why farmers know which night to put the expectant cow in the box stall, how close to empty you can trust the fuel gauge to get, when you can believe the weatherman, and how many cuttings you can harvest with a demo haybine before the dealer realizes that you are not going to buy it after all.

Artists must also manage the elements of pacing and balance. Farmers know all about these elements. Our pace is usually break-neck speed and we keep our balance by trying to keep everything from happening all at once. Like a three act play, we make every action appear effortless as we smoothly transition from one activity to the next.

So farmers really are artists whose oils are on their coveralls and whose music is the rhythm of the earth, the roar of a finely tuned tractor, and the moo of a contented cow.

I AM A FARMER

I am a psychic who must predict a month in advance the price I will be paid for the milk I sell today. I am a diplomat using every ounce of my tactful skills to keep my staff, family and neighbors happy. I am an agronomist struggling to keep my soils and crops well fed. I am a computer whiz dependent on both hardware and software to know who to breed, when to seed and where to weed. I am a plumber with enough parts and supplies on hand to repair leaks, overflows and other woes. I am an accountant seeking creative ways to balance the books in a business that buys retail and sells wholesale.

I am an electrician who must fix everything from microswitches to digital readouts and know which wires you absolutely must not touch. I am an events planner who during planting and harvesting must make sure that everything gets done, gets done right, and gets done on time. I am a dietitian constantly balancing the protein, energy and dry matter of each bite my cows eat. I am a carpenter who never has time to do it right the first time, but somehow always makes time to do it over when it breaks.

I am a detective seeking to solve the mystery of sudden production drops, machine breakdowns, and lost log chains. I am a mechanic who must face each crisis with only the tools I can carry on the tractor and who appreciates the versatility of an adjustable wrench that also can be used as a hammer, and knows the sticking power of duct tape. I am a truck driver who has learned to eat his lunch, amongst the noise and dust, while constantly double clutching.

I am a businessman who must see through savvy salesmen and glitzy gimmicks to balance the farm's needs, wants and must-haves. I am a weatherman who must decide which weather report to believe. I am a veterinarian who would rather anticipate and prevent problems than treat them. I am an animal lover who has learned that all animals respond to gentle care and kindness and that they can only show emotions by licking and kicking. I am a fashion model with manure on my pants, blood on my shirt and oil stains on my cap.

I am a neighbor who has learned the importance of treating everyone as I want to be treated. I am a parent, grateful for the opportunity to raise my family on a dairy farm. I am proud to be all of these people because I am proud to say, "I am a farmer."

STINGY OR TIGHT?

Farming isn't easy. Maintaining machinery, raising crops, and caring for cattle all take good management skills. Some farmers are good managers, some are tight with their money and some are just plain stingy. One old farmer I knew was all three.

If there ever was a way to avoid spending money he would find it. For instance, he rarely bought nails, preferring to straighten old bent ones. He has been known to take a Ziploc bag to the-all-you-can-eat church supper. He was so tight he used duct tape to patch his pants, he rarely called the vet, and even cut his own hair.

One time he needed to replace his mowing machine. His was a small farm, so buying any farm machinery new would be quite a financial burden. So I was surprised to see a new mower sitting in his yard that spring. It turns out he went to the John Deere dealer, told them he was in the market for a new mowing machine but that he couldn't make up his mind which brand would best fit his needs. He proceeded to talk the dealer into letting him try one out to cut his hay crop.

When the farmer returned it at the end of the season, the John Deere salesman asked him how he liked it and if he wanted to buy it. The farmer said that it worked ok, but he needed to try the New Holland unit first to compare, which he did the following season. This, of course, was followed by the Case IH mower, and the New Idea mower, followed by the Heston mower the following year, and so on and on.

After eight years the farmer had tried all the different mowing machines that any dealer would lend him. He finally decided that he liked the John Deere best. So, unbeknownst to any of the dealers, the next spring he bought a used one at a local auction, for less than half the price of a new one.

Is he stingy, tight, or just a good manager? I'll let you decide. I've got to go to an auction.

BEWARE OF EAR PIERCING NOISE

Farming is a noisy business. No one has to tell you that prolonged exposure to any noise can endanger your hearing. A recent study shows a majority of farmers suffer from some degree of hearing loss.

However with me, a lifetime of operating noisy farm machinery has had a completely different effect. For example, the other night my wife served me a new dish involving baked beans, curry and cucumbers. When asked how I liked it, I diplomatically mumbled something about how it wasn't going to become one of my favorites. "Well," she maintained, "You liked it the last time." I have no recollection at all of having tasted this concoction ever before. My only explanation is that prolonged exposure to roaring engines and clattering vacuum pumps has left me memory-impaired.

Another time I forgot what was planted on one of our fields that was out of sight of the barns. You can imagine my amazement when I got there with the haybine and found a wonderful crop of ten-foot high field corn, which I had planted last spring.

That's right, if I had spent my life in a quiet office or automobile, I might now be able to remember where I left the good log chain or which field I planted the sweet corn around. But, alas, by carelessly not wearing hearing protection or replacing that muffler sooner, I am now unable to recite all the presidents in order or remember the year my son was born.

So, I beseech you, do not wind up like me. Whenever you operate roaring farm machinery or are exposed to loud noises,

like the monotonous whine of a forage harvester or the throb-
bing beat of a rock concert over a mile away, wear hearing
protection of some kind.

It is easy to tell if extended exposure to noise has already
affected you. Ask yourself these questions. Do you have trouble
remembering names? How about your children's names? Your
wife's name? Better reach for those earplugs.

DOZING OFF

Farmers are the most misunderstood people in the world, perhaps because theirs is a business that sells wholesale but buys retail. It is hard to understand how anyone could choose to produce a perishable product that often is sold before the selling price is known. I am not saying that farmers are crazy, just that they are hard to understand.

Take the common situation in which farmers often find themselves. This all-season phenomenon occurs when farmers attend some sort of crowded gathering. It could be a farm meeting sponsored by Cooperative Extension or Farm Bureau, or a church service, or even a family reunion. After sitting for a while inside a warm building, most farmers will appear to – how shall we say it – doze off. Now to the speaker, clergy or matriarch, this may appear to be rude and insensitive behavior but this is not the case at all.

We have to remember the many frustrations, oops, I mean challenges, which that farmer had to face that day before he rushed into the house, got cleaned and changed and sped off to this crowded event. It could have been anything from frozen pipes to jelled fuel filters, but whatever it was, it caused the farmer to fall into a state bordering on comatose. Actually the farmer was just employing a tactic known as 'relaxation therapy'.

To the untrained eye this appears to be simply dozing off, or to put it more crudely, falling asleep. That is a vast oversimplification of what actually happens. In reality, this is a technique perfected by many farmers to let their memories select only the good things to remember and let all the bad things simply dissolve into space. It is actually a well-developed meditation stance often only achieved by Buddhist monks.

The real trick is to be so relaxed that your mind can still function but yet not so relaxed that you fall out of your chair or, even worse, jerk your head with an audible grunt, quickly glancing around to see if anyone noticed.

Perfecting this technique is often the only way farmers can reconcile themselves to a vocation that is so challenging that only those skilled at "relaxation therapy" can succeed.

WHITE PANTS

I'll never be able to wear white pants. It's all right. I've accepted it. It is one of the many choices available to others, but just not a possibility for me. Oh, maybe on show day at the fair, but even then, before the day is half over, those beautiful white pants will be covered with green splash spots, greasy fingerprints and traces of bovine saliva. At a fair these mishaps are understandable and accepted.

I'm talking about wearing white pants on those rare times a farmer gets dressed up. Within minutes of donning them a black smudge will appear as if by magic, then shortly after that a multi-colored stain will attach itself to my left pant leg. Where do all these offending adornments come from?

The only explanation I can think of is, after years of using my work denims as a combination wiping rag, blotting tissue, napkin, Kleenex and all-purpose towel, I have formed some less than admirable habits. For example, when checking the engine oil level on a tractor far from the shop, where else would you wipe the oily dipstick than on a pant leg? Or, say you quickly rinsed your hands after taking a cow's temperature, where else could you readily dry them than on the seat of your pants?

As the legs of my dungarees gradually darken with remnants of grease, blood and manure, I marvel at any farmer who sports Bermuda shorts to work in. For me they wouldn't provide enough surface to wipe my hands on. I envy the tradesmen who pass through my barn, including electricians, carpenters and plumbers, who manage to keep their khaki Carhartt pants free from telltale spots and blemishes. But then, they don't work around neatness-challenged bovines like I do.

Some farmers and even veterinarians have remedied the problem by opting for coveralls. As a fashion statement I look much more like a football in them than a catalog model. Besides, they don't soak up the stains as well as denims do.

The next time you come by the farm don't be surprised to see me in my jeans. You will never catch me working in Bermuda shorts or wearing white pants.

TYPES OF FARMERS

We all know that farmers are different but did you know that farmers fall into four personality types? This is an important bit of knowledge that can help us better understand why some farmers act the way that they do.

The first is the "DRIVER." This type is a high energy, get as much done as possible in the shortest possible time person, with a short attention span. They can be recognized by not having time to visit right now and by suddenly turning and walking away while you are explaining something long and intricate, because they just thought of something that had to be done right then. If you want to talk to them, condense your whole story into a concise two-minute sound bite or else you will be watching their back disappear into the barn.

The second type is called "AMIABLE." They are usually the youngest children in a large family who have learned to survive by agreeing with whatever the driver in the family wants. This farmer is the type that salesman love because he avoids confrontation at all costs. They often agree to do things that they had no interest in doing in the first place. This need to keep things peaceful usually results in good marriages. These people are easy to get along with, but just once we would like to know what **they** really think.

"ANALYTICAL" is the third category. This type loves math, likes to scrutinize things and needs all kinds of supporting statistics before they make a decision. Don't expect them to decide anything in a hurry. These are the people who vacillate so much at an auction that by the time they decide to bid the auction is closed. Yet they will happily spend hours detailing the numerous reasons why the self-cleaning manure spreader they just bought was such a good deal.

Everybody's favorite is the "OUTGOING." These are the back-slapping, upbeat, name-remembering, and talk-your-arm-off kind of people who make you feel comfortable. Just once it would be nice if they would let you say something, anything. Don't stop to visit them unless you've got all day. But you will get the full farm tour, including the remodeled milking parlor, state of the art tractor complete with a refrigerator in the cab, and their new remote control lawnmower.

This key to personality types should make it easier to understand why and how farmers are different. Can you decide what personality type you are? I'm amiable, so if it is all right with you it's all right with me. I've got to go now, my wife is dragging me to a hooked rug show.

YOUR FARM FROM THE AIR

If you ever have the opportunity to view your farm from the air, jump at the chance. Don't worry, I don't mean literally. My prayers were answered when I was invited to go up in a small two-seater, Volkswagen-powered collection of pipe, canvas, Plexiglas and luck. What an experience! Nothing can duplicate the feeling of seeing the ground fall away beneath you as you roar into the realm of birds and clouds, crammed into a cockpit the size of a motorcycle sidecar.

From the air everything looks flat. Those steep hills seem to recede and gentle slopes disappear. I could hardly wait to see my picturesque farmstead from the air. I envisioned the red barns standing proudly, arranged neatly amid my well-kept fields and pastures. At an altitude of 600 feet, my farm appeared on the horizon.

Those hills that I feared to climb on a tractor with a baler and wagon in tow now seemed like a flat canvas. I marveled at how different the farm looked from above. It was as if I were viewing a calendar photo or a farm magazine cover, shot in the beautiful level fields of Ohio or Iowa. Wow, what a difference a few hundred feet make!

Then it dawned on me. From this perspective there were no secrets. Every junk pile, discarded piece of black plastic and rusty obsolete machine came into plain view. What I thought was a show place was actually a collection of rusty roofs, haphazardly placed tractors and crooked corn rows.

Snapping madly with my automatic camera in one hand while clinging to the window ledge with the other, I made a vow to pick things up, to park machinery in neat rows, and to try to make my corn rows straighter. But then, as we were landing, I asked myself who would see the fruits of my efforts? Certainly not airline pilots as they fly too high and are too busy to sightsee and definitely not military aircraft as they are too concerned with training exercises.

In reality, it would be only air tourists like myself who would appreciate my efforts to tidy up, and, since most farmers are too busy to fly anyway, I think I'll not worry about those messy items. Boy, am I glad that you can't see an aerial view of my office!

THINGS A FARMER WILL NOT DO

I firmly believe that you can always tell a farmer, but you can't tell him much. That's because farmers are stubborn (oops, I mean strong willed), a trait almost necessary to succeed in a profession that would defeat a person with less fortitude.

As amiable as most farmers are, there are certain things farmers will not do. For example, a farmer will never tell you directly how much something cost, especially if he doesn't want to admit that purchasing it in the first place was a mistake. A farmer will not go around the long way if he thinks there is any chance he can get through the mud hole on the short cut. He will never take advice from someone who has never actually done it himself.

He will never buy anything from a salesman who says you should buy one because your neighbor did, who talks too long about himself and who calls the farmer by his first name one too many times. A farmer will not work out or go to the gym even though he might walk six miles and get on and off a tractor over 20 times a day.

A farmer will not go to a flower show, quilt show or display of plastic gnomes unless they have a tractor pull there, too. He will not take time to go for a hammer as long as an adjustable wrench, large draw pin or a rock is close at hand.

A farmer will not do anything if he thinks he is being pushed into it, like washing his car, going to church or buying a cemetery lot. He will never admit he is wrong as long as there is a reason to blame the mistake on someone else. He will not take time to change his barn clothes if he is only going for parts, supplies or ice cream.

He will not believe the fuel gauges on his tractors, feeling that a dipstick is more accurate. A farmer will not buy anything he can make, nor make anything he can buy.

And last of all, a farmer will not try anything new unless he thinks it was his idea first.

MY BIG MOMENT

A farmer is never prepared for this. No amount of college training or work experience can give you the resources necessary to cope with this challenge. When the call comes even the hardiest of farmers have been known to wilt. Am I talking about a call from your mother-in-law, the I.R.S. or, worse yet, the milk inspector? No, nothing as mundane or as trivial as that.

It was the news director at the local television station. "Would I be home this afternoon? Would I be willing to make a few comments on a local story about the problems farmers face? Would it be all right if a reporter and camera crew stopped by the farm later?" I readily agreed, feeling that farmers should always jump at any opportunity to explain their side of the story.

Then I suddenly asked myself, "What should I wear?" I wanted all those viewers watching from their dinner tables to believe that farmers produce a clean, wholesome product. However, sometimes it is impossible to stay spotlessly clean on a farm. If my clothes were too clean no one would believe that I really am a farmer.

Whenever I see a color photo in a magazine of a farmer standing in his barn wearing spotless jeans and a freshly pressed red and white checkered shirt, I say to myself, "This guy had plenty of notice that the photographer was coming." If I ever wore a red and white shirt to the barn, it would be a signal for all my cows to raise their tails in unison and wait for me to come within firing range. No, a button-down collar shirt and new jeans just wouldn't be believable.

As I was exploring other possible ensembles, I spotted a car with big TV News letters all over it, pulling into my yard. That gave my clothing decision some degree of urgency. I made a snap decision, the kind good farmers are famous for. It was obvious my everyday work clothes would make my profound comments more relevant, so I simply washed the manure from my boots and reached for a new seed corn hat I had been saving for such an occasion. You see, farmers use hats, the same way well dressed women use scarves, more as an accessory than for warmth. Properly dressed, I was ready to face the TV camera, without a trace of fear.

A lot of good it did. My TV debut turned out to be a 30 second voice-over shot of my cows staring at the cameraman. I guess I should have worn black and white!

EXERCISE

I recently read an article, in a farm magazine no less, promoting the idea that no matter how hard one works on a farm, there is no substitute for a formal, organized exercise program. I've read articles like this before, but never in a so-called farm publication. I have always discounted such stories written by health nuts who regard "work" as a four-letter word.

Most experts agree that the best exercise for people my age is walking. That means if I walk the length of my barn several times a day, which I do, and if, during milking, I walk the length of the milking parlor a minimum of a whole lot of times, I must easily walk two, maybe even three miles a day.

Another highly touted exercise is climbing stairs or at least pretending to climb stairs. That's great, because I must climb the equivalent of a four-story building everyday just climbing on and off tractors. Most tractors require two or three steps to mount or dismount. I always add a few steps to my count because the steps on a tractor are much steeper than normal stairs and require greater effort to climb. Just mounting a tractor gives the thighs, wings and drumsticks a thorough aerobic workout.

Then there are 'squats'. This is the flexing of the upper or lower thigh – I forgot which – but it is accomplished by bending your knees while keeping the backbone upright. This maneuver strengthens all kinds of muscles necessary to impress other health nuts. I get to do a squat every time I drop something. Fortunately for my upper or lower thighs, I drop a lot of things: in the shop it is wrenches, in the parlor it is the dip cup, on a ladder it is usually my hammer and at the dinner table it is my fork and sometimes even my green beans.

So, you see, I have my own exercise program. It includes aerobic and anaerobic exercises, doesn't require any special clothing or equipment, and saves the cost of a trendy gym. You are welcome to come 'workout' with me any time.

FARM PROGRAMS ONLINE

I was surprised to read recently about how the diligent people at the United States Department of Agriculture are revamping their computer system so that farmers will be able to apply for government programs from the comfort of their own homes. These government pen pushers must be out of their minds!

It has taken several decades of continuous revisions by loquacious politicians, confused bureaucrats and sadistic double talk specialists to make the farm programs so complicated that even the people who administer them don't understand them. In fact, when USDA employees go bezerk from trying to read and make sense of the fine print, they usually are quietly transferred to an easy job at the I.R.S., auditing corporate tax returns or answering their 1-800 help line.

Whoever thinks that someone could understand these programs and their instructions well enough to apply for them from their home computer probably thinks milk comes from cartons, vegetables come from plastic bags and potato chips are harvested very carefully by big machines with delicate rubber fingers.

Seriously, all government programs by their very nature are complex. They are not a logical, step-by-step set of instructions, but rather an accumulations of rules, references and footnotes all designed to cover up loopholes in the law. Each time someone finds a way to get around the original intent of the law, a new subtitle is created to prevent them from doing that again. The resulting hodge-podge of rules, restrictions and random recriminations are almost impossible to read and interpret.

Another reason the government made farm programs as complex as they are is to keep the public from finding out how much it really costs to produce food. Farmers are caught in the middle, unable to pay their bills unless they apply for a myriad of overlapping schemes and contrivances provided by those whose slogan is, "I'm from the government and I'm here to help you."

So when you begin to wade into this morass of government bureaucratization online and in your pajamas, don't be like me, nearly applying to get paid for not growing bamboo, canceling all my credit cards by mistake, or, worse yet, accidentally sending the cowpox virus to their computers.

PARLOR PERSPECTIVES

My windows on the world are in the room where I spend far too much of my time, our milking parlor. Although our milking parlor has windows, you can't see much out of them. They are so small that about all you can see is whether it is day or night or if it is snowing. They aren't actually transparent either, so when a farm hand or my wife waves to me, I often fear it is a monster or a confused heifer on the loose.

When planning my parlor, I was advised to install big floor to ceiling windows because often the person working in the parlor is too isolated from all the bustling activities typical on a busy dairy farm. I was deterred by the cost and fear of breakage by a few misguided cows, bent on walking right through the plate glass. When I envisioned the large windows, the kind you could actually see through, I also pictured a large silhouette of a cow carefully positioned to prevent cows from walking into them, just as they use bird decals to keep birds from flying into your picture window.

I also began to wonder what would happen if I were privy to everything that happens on the farm. Would I regret being inside milking as I watched the relatives arrive for a poolside visit? Would I continually be running to hide when I saw a salesman pull up? Would I rather not see the errant Dion wagon smash into my parked car? Would I be sad on long winters nights as I slowly watched the lights go off in the house, one by one, knowing that my family was tucked warmly in bed while I wouldn't be in for another few hours?

No, I think I like my isolated, safe little parlor world. It is true that the person in the parlor is rather isolated from the outside world most of the time, dependent on sounds, smells and limited sights to figure out what is happening elsewhere on the farm. For example, the sound of the milk house door closing can, by the intensity of the slam, tell me who probably just arrived. If it closes gently, it is apt to be the milk truck driver; if it slams shut it is probably the milk truck driver upset because I am not done milking yet. If, however, the milk house door opens and closes noiselessly, it most likely is a burglar trying to steal my new leather gloves.

A door slam followed by a timid entry into the parlor usually means someone is visiting who only brought one pair of shoes and doesn't want to get them dirty, like a city-raised house guest, a newly hired insurance salesperson or a super model seeking road directions. Whiffs of car exhaust, unburned diesel fuel, or burning clutch are all clues to what's happening beyond my four-walled enclosure.

Besides, the best part of my tiny little opaque windows on the world is that nobody can see in. Who knows what they might catch me doing, like picking my nose, retrieving and eating a cookie that fell on the floor, or milking in my boxer shorts on a hot day.

WHY FARMERS MAKE GOOD HUSBANDS

The other day my wife came to me very upset. It seems our daughter confided in her that she was dating a farmer. I consoled my wife with the many reasons that farmers make good husbands.

Farmers will eat almost anything you put in front of them, including casseroles.

A farmer functions well on little sleep, can fix anything, and allows his wife lots of free time.

Farmers have the patience to teach their children how to drive, farm trucks and tractors, that is.

Farmers usually come with a big farmhouse, lots of land and deep roots.

Farmers know the value of a dollar and don't waste money on expensive watches.

Farmers provide lots of opportunity for exercise while tending the lawn and garden, chasing cows, and stacking wood.

Farmers live long lives and give their family lots of quality time while helping to feed calves and milk.

A farmer saves you money by changing your car's oil in the farm shop and taking you out for dinner at the free coop annual meeting.

A farmer doesn't ask you to iron his work clothes nor need an expensive wardrobe and, during harvest, he won't miss you if you go away for a weekend with the girls.

Farmers actually know how to change a tire, are too busy to follow sports and are always willing to clean up any left-over pie.

And it doesn't matter what a farmer looks like as you won't see much of him anyway.

Farmers spare you the inconvenience and disruption caused by frequent job changes. And you won't have to worry about what to pack for your vacation because you won't be taking any - unless you count farm days or a tractor show.

A farmer will always secure the best washing machine for his wife, to handle the 25 loads of farm laundry each week.

Farmers will always till your garden plot, as long as they can do it with a 5-bottom plow, leaving you with an acre or more to plant.

Farmers have faith, determination and fortitude, all needed to remain in farming and to make a marriage last.

WHY FARMERS FARM

Why do farmers farm? That's a question that most of us cannot answer easily or honestly. When asked, we usually just laugh and make up an excuse like, "I don't know how to do anything else," or "I just love the long hours, low pay, and hard work." With responses like these, farmers are simply avoiding a deeper analysis of the real reasons for their career choice.

Maybe it's the unbelievable exhilaration they get every time they deliver a calf, finish harvesting a field, save an animal's life, or make it all the way home with the chopper after running on empty for the last two hours. Maybe it's the satisfaction farmers get from seeing a building they planned finally erected, from finishing planting ahead of schedule, and from finding no broken bones after being kicked by a cow.

But, most of all, farmers love a challenge like trying to make a profit in a business that buys retail and sells wholesale. Perhaps it is the challenge of succeeding in a business that requires boundless energy, a high degree of technical and managerial skill and is totally dependent on the weather. Or possibly it's the challenge of getting as many free samples from a salesman as possible, or driving through a mud hole without getting stuck or cajoling the milk inspector into thinking things are actually cleaner than the last time they came.

But seriously, the real reasons farmers farm are that they would rather wear jeans to work than a suit and tie, they want to work on their own schedule rather than on someone else's, and they can sleep soundly knowing that their hard work and productivity helps clothe and feed the world. In addition, they enjoy having lots of excuses for not spending quality time with the in-laws.

WEDDING VOWS FOR FARMERS

A farmer and his wife have a very special bond, born from their mutual concern for both their family and their farm. These twin demands are not always made clear to a starry-eyed couple making plans for a life together. That is why a new set of wedding vows are needed just for farm couples to help them fully comprehend what they are getting themselves into.

For the non-suspecting soon-to-be bride it should read, "I take thee to be my wedded husband to have and to hold, in spite of greasy fingernails and always late for meals, from this day forward. I take you for richer and for poorer, for no new curtains and recycled mattresses, for trying to balance farm books and still keep kids in school clothes; in sickness and in health, through mild heart attacks and dirty handkerchiefs; to love and to cherish despite long hours away, thinning hair and mud on the carpet; to honor and respect you despite impulse purchases, never doing the dishes, forgotten anniversaries, few vacations, antiquated bathrooms and having to help you pull tractors out of the mud. I pledge my faithfulness as long as we both shall live, regardless of what my mother warned me about farmers."

For the lucky proud husband, the vows might sound like, "I take thee to be my wedded wife, to have and to hold through thunderstorms, cold winters and family reunions, from this day forward. I promise to love you in good times and in bad, in dry falls and wet springs; in joy as well as in sorrow, in high prices and dented fenders; in sickness and in health, through long labors and short back rubs; to love and to cherish, through meals served in the field, mad dashes for parts, burnt cookies and gray hair, to laugh with you at high school reunions and to cry with you at our children's weddings; to honor you till death does us part, as long as we both shall live, always grateful that you didn't marry the rich engineer you dated in college."

On second thought, I don't know if these special wedding vows are needed as very few farm couples ever get divorced.

YOU MUST LIVE ON A DAIRY FARM IF:

A trip to the fair is considered a vacation.

Your kitchen table is always piled high with newspapers, unopened mail, and bills.

Everything from Christmas dinner to family weddings must occur between milkings.

The doors on your pickup truck are different colors.

All your drinking glasses are milk replacer cups.

An electric fence marks the end of your backyard.

You own five Tingley boots but they're all for the left foot.

You have ever had to wash off in the backyard with a garden hose before your wife would let you in the house.

You get called before every parade to borrow your hay wagon.

Your fingers are either stained orange from teat dip or black from grease.

You have ever driven off the road while examining your neighbor's crops.

You have ever peeled an apple with the same knife you used to clean a cow's hoof.

Your wife agreed to observe Mother's Day after the corn is planted.

You have animals living in buildings more expensive than your house.

You are home before midnight on New Year's Eve because you have to be up early the next morning to milk.

You know cow pies aren't made of beef.

You have used baler twine for a belt.

You appreciate the many blessings of raising your family in the country, teaching them the value of money and the cycles of nature.

Chapter 3

WHAT THEY SHOULD TEACH YOU IN AG SCHOOL

A diploma from a prestigious agricultural college, the result of four years of intense study, experimentation and partying, should prepare one for the challenges of operating a modern, efficient and profitable farm. The key word here is **should.**

As proud as I was of my diploma and a head crammed full of facts, figures and ideas, I simply was not prepared for many situations on the farm. Although organizing your day is important, when you enter the barn in the wee hours of the morning to find a broken water pipe and the gutters and mangers full of water, with the lime truck due in a few minutes and a vacuum pump that won't start, you might ask yourself, "Is compiling a 'to do' list for that day really necessary?" Besides, I think that the joy of crossing off each item on a 'to do' list is vastly overrated.

While I did learn how to determine when a crop was ready to harvest, someone should have taught me how to harvest all of the first cutting hay crop within a five day period, at its peak nutritive value, when it usually rains two of the five days and the cows still must be fed and milked each day.

Knowing about the fertilizer value of manure is one thing, but learning how to spread it daily in snow, mud and deep water was not covered in any of my courses. It's high time that some ag economics professor develops a manure futures program whereby a dairy farmer could spread manure ahead when weather was good, so he wouldn't have to when conditions made spreading impossible. And another thing, why wasn't I told that it would take more time to repair, adjust and pound on farm machines than it does to actually use them?

What we really need is a course in understanding how a cow thinks or, should I say, doesn't think. Countless hours could have been saved if only I had known that cows have eyes on the sides of their heads, which is why they can't see the parlor door right in front of them, or that cows always go the opposite way you want them to go. And why wasn't I told that one cow, when sufficiently provoked, can produce enough manure to fill a small minivan.

If I were designing the curriculum for an ag school, I'd make sure each four-year program included five years of farm experience. Then, and only then, graduates just might be prepared to be a farmer.

MYSTERY SOLVING

Most of what a farmer does is really mystery solving. Why did this happen? How did that happen? It's the secret of what makes a good mechanic or a good veterinarian. Simply put, "You have to know how something works before you can diagnose why it is not working."

The biggest mystery we have to solve on our farm is how to stop all the leaks on our tractors. Today's tractors are a modern marvel of balanced powerful engines and fast smooth hydraulic systems. To make all this happen requires half a barrel of oil to be sprayed, sloshed and pumped through a myriad of channels, galleys, tubes and hoses, most of it at very high pressure.

When everything is right none of it will spray, drip or seep out of its proper place within the mysterious innards of the machine. But alas, with daily wear, tear and breakage, most of our tractors soon show signs of not being able to hold their oils. The worst case of course is the 'big leak,' which involves a major stream of hydraulic oil spraying directly into the radiator fan blades. Fortunately, a leak of this size is easily detected when your glasses, shirt and the whole rear half of the tractor suddenly become covered with a slimy film of oil.

More pesky are the smaller leaks that manifest themselves with those golden drops of oil dripping one by one off the lowest point on the machine. Where do they come from? Finding the actual leak is the hard part, as you gaze into the engine area and all that can be seen is a layer of oil soaked silage covering everything. To find the actual source of the leak requires washing the entire front half of the tractor with a high-pressure hose.

Then the real detective work begins. One has to notice every nook and cranny, every incriminating detail, every gasket surface, and every hose connection. Now it is time to question the evidence, asking "Is that crack in the heater hose new, or has it been their all along?", "Does that 'O' ring look suspiciously shriveled?" or "Is the thermostat housing really cracked or has the paint started to chip?" After a thorough examination of all the possible suspects, if the culprit cannot be found, sadly, we just add more oil and keep going.

Since farming requires so much detective work, we try to fix all our major leaks and put-off solving the minor ones.

MULTI-TASKING

Did you ever notice how efficiently a good waitress takes care of several tables at once in a busy family-style restaurant? She makes every trip past your table count. She rarely wastes a motion, always seeing that your water glass is full, your coffee hot, and your breadbasket brimming with warm rolls, all while busily delivering orders to other customers.

I can't help but feel that this same ability to multi-task is required to milk cows in a one person milking parlor. Farmers have always been able to do more than two jobs at once. Trying to prep and milk on one side while finishing and dipping cows on the other requires the same balancing act as remembering all the orders for a party of six at one table while keeping everyone happy at several other tables. Just as I need to attach each milker unit within one minute of prepping and wiping each cow, a waitress must greet each new table of guests within three minutes of their arrival, provide them with the correct number of menus, and take their beverage orders.

Hungry people and cows with full udders can both be impatient and demanding. The big difference is in how we handle their needs. A waitress must be accommodating, patient, and cheerful while I only need to be gentle, competent and avoid getting stepped on.

Just as I must deal with the moods of each cow and patiently reattach any units that get kicked off, a good waitress must know how to handle people and deal with the attitudes of those customers who are not happy with the meal they ordered. She must also tolerate the changing moods of the busboy and a temperamental cook in order to get her orders out quickly enough to be assured of good tips. We both have to deal with regulars. Hers expect her to know that they want double cream with their coffee. Mine expect me to let them in first on the same side of the parlor or not at all.

Of course, I don't have to force myself to be pleasant to people I may never see again just to get a tip, but I still have to be nice to the cows I see day after day in hopes that they will give me that extra pound or two of milk.

On the plus side, a waitress gets to work year-round in a warm, dry and fairly clean environment while I don't have to run myself ragged trying to please a steady stream of hungry people. If only I had a busboy to run errands and clean up after me and a cook to make me look good!

Since farmers are so good at multi-tasking, maybe while I am milking I could do research on the Internet, wash the parlor walls, and even teach the cows how to reupholster furniture. I wonder what else I could do while milking.

DIFFERENCES

It takes a lot of give and take to make a marriage work on a farm. In my case my wife does most of the giving. That's not my fault, though. She is just able to see things that I can't. I used to think it was x-ray vision, but I am beginning to think it's just that men and women see things differently.

For example, if my wife finds out ahead of time that the accountant is coming, she will vacuum all the carpets in the house, wax the kitchen floor, scrub all the counters and the kitchen table, make a coffee cake to serve and then place a small vase of fresh flowers on the table. However, if I know that he is coming, I just wait until he arrives, invite him in, simply sweep all the magazines, newspapers and cats from the kitchen chairs and sit down and go to work.

It is the same way when we both look at the lawn. She can look at our lawn after it comes alive in the spring and see patches of tall grass, lots of dandelions, bare spots, and occasional snow plow gouges and then fret about how much work it will take to get it into shape before the next family party. Me? I'm just glad it's green. I'll get the lawn mower out when we finish haying.

The carpet in my office is another problem. Like most farm offices, it also is the cloak room, mudroom and rear entrance to the house. That's why it is sometimes hard to keep the carpet clean enough for company to see. She doesn't understand that the coins scattered around are there in case I need to stop for ice cream on the next trip I take for parts or that the barn shoes by my desk are really cleaner than they look. I do vacuum the carpet at least once a year.

We even clean the bathroom differently. She spends hours scrubbing and polishing while I just pick up any large objects lying on the floor like towels, magazines and bicycles, flush the toilet and shout, "I'm done!"

Why these contradictions in our points of view? I guess, like most men, I just don't care if the kitchen is immaculate, the lawn perfect, the office carpet vacuumed, and the bathroom clean and tidy. My mind is preoccupied with more important things, like where the next tractor pull is, when the next all-you-can-eat buffet is, or why muddy footprints on a white tile floor are such a big deal.

OPTIMISTS AND PESSIMISTS

I have long wondered why some people are always cheerful and others are not. Is it the way they were brought up? Is it because they always look on the bright side of anything that may happen to them? Is it what they ate for breakfast?

I have a theory that may answer these questions. Simply put, people have learned to use either a positive or negative attitude as a crutch to get themselves through life. The cheerful, optimistic ones cope by smiling, making little jokes, always being thankful no matter the calamity that befalls them, and saying, "It could have been worse." The spilled coffee didn't burn them, the flat tire was discovered before they got on the thruway or the fall down the stairs only broke two ribs. I can't help but think these people have insulated themselves from adversity. No matter what happens, "It could have been worse."

Then there are those who seem to have been born with a negative attitude implanted in their brains. These consummate pessimists have found that no matter what happens to them, "It wasn't my fault." Since childhood they have been blaming poor grades on teacher favoritism, lack of success on the job on the boss's incompetence, and failures in relationships on others expecting them to be perfect.

It is no surprise that most successful farmers are born optimists. Why else would anyone pin their hopes on a business that is defined by low prices, high costs and fickle weather. Optimists have the ability to visualize themselves succeeding, regardless of the stacks of bills in the mailbox, muddy fields on the flats and impending thunderstorms over the freshly mown hay. Optimists view these not as obstacles, but as opportunities.

For farmers, being a pessimist is detrimental. Farming is about growing and changing, yet pessimistic farmers are reluctant to try anything new for fear that it won't work, will be a rip off, or worse yet, that they will fail entirely.

These farmers have only two choices: they can lumber along accepting their lot in life, or realize that the only road to success is to become more optimistic, even if only a little at a time.

I don't think it is possible to change a pessimist into an optimist in one lifetime. I'm just glad I was born an optimist.

CHANGED ENVIRONMENT

One of the casualties of fewer farms and more people moving to the country is the traditional farm supply store. When I started farming, every rural village had a business that tried very hard to serve the needs of the farmers in the area. Going into one of these stores was akin to a child going into a candy store. We wanted one of everything but could only afford what we specifically came for.

As we walked past rows of wheelbarrows, bags of fertilizer and calf grain, and entered the store we were hit with the unique aroma of a mixture of mothballs, new pitchforks and molasses-coated grain. The shelves were laden with everything from canning jars to fence staples. Shiny new manure shovels, barley forks and hoes with paint covering their blades hung from hooks on the walls. Over in the corner were spools of barbed wire, tools such as fence stretchers and staple pullers, and, of course, fence pliers. On the outside wall work clothes hung over the boxes of boots with felt liners.

You could buy anything for the farm there, from milker inflations to chain repair links. There was always a big selection of work gloves of every type and leather mittens with wool liners. We used to think mittens kept our hands warmer than gloves. Our lives are too precise now for mittens. We wouldn't be able to use a cell phone or palm pilot.

Over the last few decades farm stores have suffered the same attrition as farms. Only a few remain. They still serve farmers, but to stay in business, they also cater to our new non-farm rural residents. It dawned on me recently how far our store had gone to serve its new clientele.

The first clue was the preponderance of dog, cat and bird food. There were three aisles of dog food alone. Then came the birdseed, bird feeders and birdhouses. I half expected to see a selection of songbirds. I won't even go into how much horse feed, horse medicines and horse tools they had, along with model horses, barns and farm implements. Then there were the garden supplies, tools, seeds and sprays. I did find some milker inflations over in back by the black and white spotted mailboxes.

I will have to admit that a large selection of gloves was still there, although the white ones with the floral pattern were not something a farmer would ever buy. There was also a good selection of winter coats and boots. It must be that everyone needs to keep warm, whether you are filling a bird feeder, or feeding one horse, a few sheep or several hundred cows.

I should have realized how much things had changed when I first pulled in. The front of the store was covered with hanging flower baskets. I could hardly make my way through the maze of baled peat moss, ceramic lawn ornaments and carboys of pool chemicals, to get into the store itself. I'm happy though, as long as they still carry the things I need. And besides, I now know where all those garden gnomes come from.

MY 'TO DO' LIST

I think I'm gradually losing my mind. The other day I made a long, well organized, and thoughtful 'To Do' list.

The first task on the list was to spread a load of manure fresh from cleaning the barn that morning. While I was in the office getting my gloves, I discovered that the last calf born had never been ear tagged, so I took the tags and tag pliers out to her hutch and ear tagged the calf. On my way back to the barn I glanced in the barrel of calf grain and saw that it was empty, so I went to the lower barn and got a bag of pellets to replenish the barrel. Then, as I entered the office to return the tagging pliers, the phone rang. My daughter's car had a strange squeak in it. She wanted me to diagnose it from 300 miles away. It is nice to be needed but I didn't have the slightest idea what caused the noise.

Dreading going back out into the cold to spread the manure, I put on my sweatshirt. While tying the string on the hood, I saw a list of cows that needed glue-on heat detectors as they were predicted to come in heat soon, so I headed out to search for those cows. During my search I found another cow caught in a free stall. I had to go out to the shop to get the cordless saw to cut a two by six to set her free.

Heading to the shop to return the saw I noticed that the mineral self-feeder was empty. This led me to the tool shed where I located a pail of salt and a pail of bicarb and lugged them back into the barn. As I was filling the mineral feeder I discovered a cow in heat. Quickly I ran back to the office, only to find the standing cow was too fresh to be bred at this time. After entering her heat date in the computer, I again put my gloves on, and started out the door. I spotted the milk truck pulling out of the driveway. So once again I removed my gloves and went through the steps to start the automatic washer for the milk tank. Then, I put on my gloves once more and started for the door.

By now I couldn't remember what I was setting out to do. Worse yet, I'd lost my 'to do' list and forgotten where I left the saw. No wonder I don't get anything done.

FASTIDIOUS FACES

The bunker or trench silo provides the most economical way to store and preserve large volumes of silage on today's modern, progressive dairy farms. This method of storing silage horizontally in trenches in the ground or above the ground in bunkers has proved to be very economical and efficient. As beneficial as they are to a farm's success, trench silos also present some management problems that must be solved. It requires a great deal of skill to properly remove enough silage to feed all the animals on the farm every day.

As the silage is fed out, the wall of silage remaining is called the 'face'. In most cases, it is usually over ten feet high and over 20 feet wide. Most experts recommend removing at least four inches of material from the face everyday to prevent any mold from forming that would decrease palatability and hurt feed quality.

How carefully and meticulously that face is maintained is an excellent to guide to how precise, particular and persnickety that farmer is. For example, if that wall of silage is just as straight and smooth as if it had been cut with a knife, you can be sure that the farmer does everything else just as painstakingly. He probably keeps his barns freshly painted, keeps his shop floor spotlessly clean and even keeps his sock drawer all sorted by color and size.

If that trench face is jagged and irregular as if a blind front-end loader operator had been randomly jabbing at it, unearthing large piles of silage and leaving cow-sized caverns in the face, chances are this guy is not very careful with anything he does. Don't be surprised if, on this farm, you see other signs of a lack of concern for details, like manure spreaders with flat tires, tractors with broken mufflers, and picnic tables without tablecloths. All of this moral decay and decadence could be avoided if only a proper face was maintained on their trench silo.

Judge carefully, for sometimes those who keep a neat trench face may fool you. Often that is the extent of their attention to detail. Always check those spreader tires, tractor mufflers and picnic tables first before you make any judgments.

The moral is, take time to evenly remove that four inches of silage all across the face of your silo. Don't let the neighbors see a poorly maintained face or your face might be red.

PERSONALITY PROFILES

Have you ever wondered why people's personalities differ so much? Why are some people high achievers and seemingly born leaders, others more amiable, pleasing negotiators while still others love to entertain but have a fear of rejection combined with an obvious short attention span?

I think I have stumbled onto at least a partial explanation for these differences. It is the science of birth order. According to this theory your personality is influenced by your position in the family. It turns out that whether you were first born, middle, last born or an only child makes a tremendous difference in how your personality develops and thus how you interact with others.

Firstborns and only children, for example, often live with a sense of entitlement and superiority and feel they must be in control. That should make them good farmers because having the confidence that you have made the right decision is essential in the difficult role of farm manager. The down side of being a first-born is that they lack sensitivity. I ought to know, I married one. (Oops, forget I said that.) Still, I think many of our most successful farmers are first borns.

Middle borns, because they are caught between older and younger siblings, hate confrontation, are very calm and have learned to roll with punches. They tend to be good-natured, down-to-earth and great mediators and negotiators. However, they are more eager to be liked and are not good at making decisions that will offend others. They become excellent leaders because they understand the art of negotiation, compromise and giving something for something else. Middle borns should be good at managing the farm labor force. Their ease at making friends and low-key personality might mean fewer temper tantrums, walkouts on Christmas Eve, and tomato fights in the garden.

Last borns are very special people. I'm not saying that because I am a youngest child, but rather that studies show that last borns are the world's cheerleaders, have strong people skills and love to entertain and talk to others. This innate desire to 'get along' gives them the ability to work well with farm salesmen, consultants and floral designers. Unfortunately they also get bored quickly, have a strong fear of rejection and tend to have a short attention span. They often pursue creative ventures but lack discipline in financial decisions. Some say a general lack of responsibility is the fatal flaw of youngest children. My wife would certainly agree with that.

How can we use this information to better understand our relations with others? The most important role birth order plays is in the choice of a mate. Experience shows that first borns shouldn't marry first borns, as they will always struggle to be in charge. As one perceptive first-born wife who married an oldest child said, "Our marriage is a struggle to see who can do it first and to see who gets credit for it." When two youngest marry, financial problems often occur and when two middle borns marry both are such promoters of tranquility that communication can become a real problem.

I have the best of both worlds since I am a youngest who married an oldest who likes to be in control and I let her think she is.

FARM FRIENDLY OLYMPICS

After watching the Olympic games I couldn't help but wonder why so few farmers qualified. Perhaps the traditional sports just don't have enough fascination for hard-driving agrarian youth. Maybe some new sports could be added which would be more appealing to farmers. The 'tire toss' comes to mind. This could be a timed event to see how many tires could be tossed on a trench silo in a five-minute period. Aspirants for this competition could train on as many silos as they could find.

For a relay, try the 'chasing loose heifers' event. This is most competitive if done after dark in a yard covered with snow over ice. Practicing this sport in warm weather may sharpen both physical and tactical skills but is not a substitute for the real thing.

A synchronized sport might be the 'line the truck up with the dump wagon' event. Points will be deducted for either getting too close or too far away. This one will be hard to practice for since each truck and dump wagon is different. Only those with the most practice would qualify.

The venue most farmers would excel at is the 'barn to car marathon,' in which a farmer must come in the house from the barn covered with a mixture of sweat, manure and hydraulic oil, and, in less than four minutes, must eat supper, shower, get dressed and be in the car ready to leave for a church supper or farm meeting. Optional additions for this event are shaving for men and donning panty hose for women.

These might be enough new venues for the next Olympic games, although the 'hiding from a salesman' and 'speed of milker attachment' are also possibilities. With sports like these more farmers will participate in the next Olympiad.

MANURE MUSINGS

We have been working with a crop consultant for several years, so when it became fashionable for farms to have a nutrient management plan we thought we were all set. However we had to send a sample of the manure from our free stall barn to be analyzed for nutrient content. Our consultant had the embarrassing experience of having one of his samples burst in transit. Neither he, the people at the lab, nor the U.S. Postal Service were too happy about that! Fortunately our samples arrived ok.

We went through all this trouble to determine the nitrogen, phosphorous, potash and total solids content of our manure, our most abundant farm product. The results showed that our fields needed little or no commercial fertilizer. That saves us money and reduces the risk of pollution from the run off from our fields.

I often wonder if the analysis of the manure from our cows varies with what they are fed, or the time of the year the sample is taken. I also wonder, after taking the time to gather these odiferous samples, just what goes on at that laboratory? How does one go about the unpleasant job of testing mineral content of excrement? Is it like the sterile labs of the culinary school, where men and prim, dour-looking ladies carefully assay a sample? Do they first look at its presentation in the plastic tube looking to see if the overall presentation and texture is uniform and colorful? And just what can be discerned from the bouquet of fresh Holstein manure? Can they smell the difference between feeding the first and second cutting of hay? Can they determine the added ingredient to our feed that ensures that our milk has a high fat content? Or, can they tell if I have sulfur water? You can tell I have too much time on my hands when I worry about things like that.

Next to milking, manure handling is the most time consuming job on the farm. We clean the cow barn everyday, and the heifer barn two to three times a week, making over 400 big loads of manure to be spread on our fields each year. That's a lot of time watching manure flying across our fields from the comfort of our heated and air-conditioned tractor cab. Still, with every load I take out I love the money I'm saving on fertilizer, and the image of the great crop of corn or hay that this load will help produce. Besides all the time I spend hauling manure around keeps me from going to garage sales or bookstores where I might buy something foolish.

I hope all the work, trouble and mess we go through to determine how good our manure is pays off. With manure quality as such a focus, it occurred to me that flies really are the experts. Maybe we should ask them where the best stuff is.

AVOIDING BOREDOM

Farmers like to think of themselves as being their own boss. They picture themselves as creative self-starters who meet and conquer many challenges daily. That's the good news. The bad news is that the care of crops, machines and animals requires the completion of many repetitive tasks daily.

So how does one keep an active, intelligent and inquisitive mind from becoming totally bored while doing these recurring tasks? The best way I have found is to vary the way I do things just enough so as to see them from a new perspective. One way is to do the daily jobs in a different order occasionally just to shake up my boredom barometer.

For example, every morning after the cows are safely in the holding area, I scrape both the feed alley and the free stall alley and push the manure into the spreader. Some days I'll cheat and scrape the free stall alley first and then the feed alley. When I do things like this, I always get a little guilty thrill.

This same principle applies to mowing a field of hay. I have been mowing most of my fields three or four times a year for over 40 years, but I am always overcome with a feeling of discovery when I change my plan of attack. Sometimes I will mow a big field by going around and around it several times. The next time, for variety, I may cut it into three pieces so that there are more long runs and fewer turns. I might even become bold enough to mow it north to south and another time from east to west. The feeling of excitement from making these changes is much better than I would get from going off a ski jump or running the rapids in the Grand Canyon. I am seriously considering mowing my fields diagonally this year, if I get up enough courage. I don't care what the neighbors think.

Do you get the idea now of how exhilarating it is doing routine tasks a little differently each time? This principle applies to any routine task, even running errands. We always take a different route to the John Deere dealer just to keep from getting bored, with the added benefit of keeping up with what other farmers are doing.

Just remember, there are some things we must never change. They are: never change the order that you milk and feed your cows, never wait until you have time to fill the tractor fuel tank, and never try to squeeze in one more job when you are already late for a dinner date.

STUCK IN A RUT

For many years I farmed with tractors that were old enough to vote and underpowered, but were paid for. Those old John Deere A's and Farmall M's were rugged, dependable and, above all, loyal. They handled the machines of the time well, except for a loaded manure spreader in that dreaded mud season in late March and early April. That's the period every spring when it takes over a month to go from frozen to dry tillable ground. This is one of the most difficult times farmers face.

As the days warm up and the rains come, even the most well drained soils can turn into a sea of unforgiving, bottomless brown ooze, capable of swallowing a tractor whole. Many times I have had to walk home through mud that clung to my boots and made every step a major accomplishment.

Getting one of these stuck tractors unstuck required another tractor and driver, a chain or cable long enough for the second tractor to be placed on a dry enough spot to have some traction, and patience enough to try several times to get both rigs to move in unison.

If the stuck tractor won't budge by pulling straight ahead, one must resort to the old right angle trick. Years of experience have taught us that for some reason, perhaps something to do with Bernoulli's principle, if a tractor is pulled at right angles to the direction in which it was going, quite often the stuck tractor will bounce, claw, and chew its way out of those deep ruts it dug and clamber out onto the dry ground as if nothing had happened. If that doesn't work, other alternatives are to put a for sale sign on it, turn it into a giant planter, or simply wait for summer.

I'm glad those days are gone forever. No, I haven't found a way to stop the spring rains or to prevent the saturated season of fickle frostlessness. Our secret is a four-wheel drive tractor with a cab that allows us, if we are careful, to wallow through spots that would snare a smaller two-wheel drive, bald-tired antique. This four-wheel drive tractor can climb over small buildings, knock over little trees and do everything but swim. Not that I haven't gotten it stuck before. That happened in deep snow, while going up a slight grade, when the ice beneath the snow rendered all that horsepower useless. But this time I didn't have to walk home in knee-deep snow, nor did I waste a lot of time going forward and back, getting myself into a deeper and deeper mess. No, I simply got out my cell phone, called David and read the latest farm magazine while waiting for him to come with another tractor to pull me out.

At that point I didn't know which invention I appreciated more – four-wheel drive or cell phones.

Chapter 4

BOBBLING BOTTLES

One of life's greatest miracles was the invention of the nurse bottle to feed calves. I say miracle because, for the first few years I was dairying, I foolishly thought it was possible to teach a newborn calf to drink directly from a pail from the moment of birth. This misconception usually resulted in much milk splashed all over my shirt, pants and eyebrows but very little actually inside the calf.

I knew all along that such a device as the two-quart nurse bottle existed. My reluctance to actually buy and use one stemmed from a stubborn conviction that something so simple, durable and cheap couldn't possibly work.

Being pigheaded didn't help either. But I had to find an easier way, so swallowing my pride, I finally broke down and purchased one bottle and one rubber nipple. Thus started my journey of trying to figure out how to make one work. Nobody told me that a brand new nipple was made of rubber so inflexible that most calves can't get any milk no matter how hard they suck. I began to feel sorry for the calf as she tried in vain to pull any life-giving milk from that unyielding teat.

At first I was happy because I knew the darned thing wasn't going to work. Then I was sad because I had to figure out how to get milk into that calf. I surmised a way must be found to increase the size of both the air vent and the opening at the end of the nipple. Believing in using the correct tool for each job, I chose to use what was within easy reach. Luckily I had a pole barn nail in my pocket with rough grooves cut into its full length to bite into the wood into which it would be driven. With the confidence of a fine craftsman, I deftly reamed out both holes several times with that trusty pole barn nail.

Well, that did it. The milk began to flow, the air vent let in enough air, and the calf thought this thing was the greatest invention ever! At that point, so did I.

The next greatest invention was the green wire rack to hold the nurse bottle. This contraption can be dropped over the top board of a calf pen with the bottle in it resting at a 45 degree angle, so the calf can feed itself, after finding and testing the rubber nipple.

After this discovery feeding all those calves was easy. It was just the hand washing of all those bottles that was hard. I'll have to keep doing them by hand, unless I can figure out how to run my wife's dishwasher!

CALVES AS PETS

Young dairy calves are among the cutest animals on earth. They are so cute that I don't know why they aren't more popular as house pets.

Bovine babies certainly are more appreciative than cats, although that is not saying much. Most animals are more appreciative than cats. Take dogs, for example. No matter how long you have been away, dogs are always glad to see you, with their tail wagging as if to say, "I missed you, I missed you." On the other hand, cats seem to be saying, "Well, it is about time you got back. It is almost feeding time." Fortunately, calves are more like dogs, always happy to see you. This bubbling, unbridled enthusiastic greeting is probably the calf's way of saying, "I'm hungry," but I prefer to think of it as sincere affection for the person who cares for her. Everyone should have such an upbeat loving pet.

Surprisingly, there are some disadvantages to keeping dairy calves as pets. For one thing, they only stay small, cute, and dog-size for about a month. Then, if fed properly, calves begin to grow so large that housebreaking becomes very difficult. The only way around this problem is to get a new pet calf every few weeks or frequently exchange your pet calf for a newborn one. Unless you live on a dairy farm, this could be a monumental and costly problem.

Also, it is a shame that such beautiful adorable animals, with such lovely long eyelashes and big sincere eyes, are such messy eaters, gulping their milk noisily and slurping loudly until the milk is gone. What utterly atrocious table manners!

Now that I think about it, I probably wouldn't be allowed to bring any of my new pets into the house anyway. The cat that sleeps at the foot of our bed would certainly be jealous of any newcomers. There is nothing worse than a jealous cat. Besides, my cat doesn't think of me as a friend but more as 'staff' to see to his needs.

I'm sorry to say that there are many reasons why calves would not make good pets. If they tried to sit on your lap, they would crush your thighs. They could never be taught to catch a Frisbee and never be trained to sit on command. If you had to reprimand them it would sound silly shouting a number instead of a name. Calves would eat the houseplants and, worst of all, they would have a terrible time trying to stand up on a newly waxed floor.

It is beginning to look like the idea of promoting dairy calves as house pets has too many inherent problems. I guess I'll have to forget about my pet idea and be satisfied taming each newborn calf as she comes along.

LIFE WITH COWS

As I drive through the affluent suburbs that seem to be inexorably spreading toward my farm like a slow-moving lava flow, I am struck by the thought of how lost these people must be without cows to bring some order into their lives.

Having always lived with the responsibility of caring for a herd of cows, I can't imagine what life would be like without their rigid demands. How do those without cows know when to get up in the morning or when to go to bed at night? For that matter, without cows, there is no reason to get up early.

Caring for cows has the added bonus of teaching one to be a more efficient time manager. If it weren't for their time consuming milking schedule, I never would have learned such time-savers as brushing my teeth in the shower, eating breakfast while pulling on my boots and wolfing down lunch on the tractor. Without cows there would be no reason to rush home from boring family parties or decline invitations to movies or shows that end after midnight. Without cows I would loose all track of time. I would be like someone locked underground, unable to sense whether it was night or day.

I pity those who will never have the feeling of knowing so many females so udderly dependent upon them. Besides, if we didn't have cows, I would miss those frantic calls from the barn at odd hours to pull a calf, spread a load of manure in the dark or help lift a confused cow out of the feed bunk. I would have no reason to feel guilty at missing a milking or any reason to feel the joy of sleeping late on my day off. Nor would I experience the exhilaration of finding a fresh cow standing proudly over her newborn calf or the disappointment when you find that the calf is a bull.

Having cows means that I don't have a reason to own an SUV nor waste time commuting, and my holidays are always spent close to home. No driving four states away in a snowstorm for me!

I can't help but think that if it weren't for my cows, I would face the danger of having too much leisure time and wind up like so many suburbanites squandering precious hours weeding flower beds, painting birdhouses or, worse yet, playing golf.

FROLICKING CALVES

I enjoy watching young calves run, play and test their freedom as if they were children flowing out of a school bus at day's end. Their energy and innocence allow them to be totally uninhibited just like a child.

We raise our calves in hutches until they are almost two months old. By that time they are weaned, eating some grain and silage and ready to move on to a group pen in our old barn to learn the fine art of competing with other animals for their daily grub.

The fun comes from moving them from the safe, secure and protected world of the only home they have ever known into a strange place in what to them must seem like another country with its own sights, sounds and odors. When they first discover that they are no longer tethered to a semi-permanent structure but can go anywhere and do anything within the confines of their large pen, they act like college freshman away from home for the first time. They run and jump and kick up their heels, exploring every possible hiding place within their new domain. Occasionally they stop for a minute to reflect on their good fortune that there are no limits on how they spend their time.

As soon as I leave them alone in their new paradise and am barely out of sight, the chorus of lonely cries begins. They don't realize that this is all part of a grand design to teach them to compete within a large group of similarly timid animals. To make this experience less traumatic, we first put calves into small groups of three or four. When they have learned to negotiate territory and fend for themselves in the feed bunk, we move them into larger group of eight or ten. By then they are old hands at fighting for their share of the feed and actually enjoy the company of others. To the passer-by they seem to be much more comfortable together than most family members are. It is hard then to believe they caused such a fuss when they were first introduced.

Just like people, it doesn't matter how good you have it now, it takes a little while to forget how things used to be.

ADVICE COLUMN FOR COWS

The time has come to provide, as a public service, an advice column for cows. My lifetime spent trying to solve bovine behavior problems certainly qualifies me to write such a column and to assume the title of cow psychologist.

My first letter comes from a mature, well educated and self-confident registered Holstein who writes, "I work with 200 other females in a somewhat confining situation. Trying to express my individuality and receive proper credit for my accomplishments is often difficult. How can I properly draw attention to my unique qualities and value to the entire farm operation?" Signed Prilly.

Dear Prilly: In a herd as large as yours it will always be difficult to be thought of as an individual unless you adopt a distinctive behavior characteristic. You could quietly try to sneak up behind any human who is otherwise occupied and begin to lick them in the middle of the back. This will usually startle them enough so that, when they stop running, they will surely take the time to find your ear tag number and be on the watch for you whenever they are working in the barn. If that doesn't work, you could always vigorously scratch your head on the parlor door until someone comes to find out who is making all that racket. There are many other ways to express your individuality, many of which involve breaking automatic waterers or opening gates. Good Luck.

My second question comes from a first calf heifer that is having difficulty adjusting to life as a single mother. She writes, "My best friend, Elsie, spends most of her time standing directly in front of the mineral feeder. Whenever I try to get in a lick of salt she pushes me away. How can I make her understand my needs, too? Signed Wants Some Salt.

Dear Wants Some Salt: This is a very ticklish problem that calls for some negotiating skills. A mineral feeder is meant for everyone to share equally. You might try to distract Elsie by staring into the driveway through the gate beside the mineral feeder. Soon she will run over to see what you are looking at, which gives you a chance to steal some salt, until Elsie realizes that there is nothing there and she has been duped. If this doesn't work, as a last resort, you could always belt her one in the chops to let her know you want your turn at the salt. You must make her understand that your action in no way is meant to affect your friendship, unless, of course she hauls off and belts you one back. Sometimes one's need for salt trumps one's need for friends. Good Luck.

This advice column business isn't as hard as I thought it might be!

COW TIPS

On my last trip to the mega-book store, where I love to take short naps in those wonderful overstuffed chairs, I noticed a new wave of self-help books on how to be successful in business. Many of the authors cited unique sources for their guaranteed successful ideas, such as raising earthworms made me a millionaire and applying bowling principles to the stock market.

I was not impressed. Why even I could write such a book, only I would title it, "How My Cows Taught Me To Be Successful In Business." Most people don't realize how intelligent, perceptive, and innovative dairy cows actually are. Some of the key adages in my book follow.

For example, twice a day I put my entire milking herd into the holding area just before milking. There are always a few cows who immediately line up, anxious to enter the milking parlor first. These are the leaders, the first to try something new and to show the others that there is nothing to fear. People are just like cows. Some want to be first – first to buy a new car or tractor, first to try a new farm practice or first in the neighborhood to plant corn or cut hay. We learn from this that to be successful we must recognize those who have leadership abilities but we must also be sure that they are leading us in the right direction.

Here is another principle I learned while watching my cows eat. When some cows consume the total mixed ration from the feed bunk, they spend an inordinate amount of time sorting the mix of silage and grain, trying to separate the grain portion from the mix. They do this by clearing a spot on the floor of the bunk and tumbling small portions of feed onto this cleared spot, hoping the heavier grain will fall off so they can eat this more palatable portion first. This illustrates that cows are just like people: some are better at sifting the important facts or figures from an article or report than others. From this we learn to seek advice from a higher authority as a county agent, consultant or salesman who can sort out the most important facts for us to use.

In any herd of cows or group of people there will always be a few who are forever in your way, either seeking attention or constantly underfoot. These will not be the most productive cows or people. The real strength of any herd or organization is the quiet hard working core always tending to business. For people, they are the ones who are always there, punctual, reliable and professional at all times. For cows they are either eating, being milked or chewing their cuds. When seeking new members of your team look for the quiet workers, not those constantly seeking attention.

So, you can see that working with cows can teach you a lot about being successful in business as well as in life. I can hardly wait to see what clever business principle my cows will teach me next.

CAREER COWS

Cows come and go. That's the way dairy farming is. Sometimes I am sad to see a favorite cow go; other times I secretly rejoice when that miserably-dispositioned, chronic kicker with a mean, unforgiving streak, happens to be the one to be culled.

What do I mean by favorite cows? I call them career cows. They are the ones who never give me any trouble. Their lives seems to center around eating, drinking, chewing their cuds, staring into space and waiting patiently to be milked. They are the ones who make it plain that they don't want any trouble. They slink back when they see you coming. They avoid eye contact whenever possible, hoping they will not be noticed. Somehow, they must think that 1,500 pounds of live weight, roughly the size of a small car, won't be noticed if they stand perfectly still, act unconcerned and pretend to be someone else. I have one such career cow who occasionally masquerades as another one who looks just like her. She still hasn't caught on that those pesky, unfashionable numbered ear tags are a dead giveaway to her identity.

My least favorite cows are the hyperactive, bold, and spirited ones who are always underfoot when you don't need them, and who disappear when you do need them. They spend their leisure time blocking the exit door of the parlor, pushing smaller cows away from the feed bunk, and throwing my shovel into the spreader. Their middle name is trouble. I wouldn't be surprised to see them doing summersaults down the feed alley, licking the steel pipes on a zero-degree day to see if their tongues would freeze to the pipes, or having contests to see who can run the fastest while balancing a pail of water on their head, chewing their cud and whistling, all at the same time. Unfortunately, their career goal is getting into mischief, not making milk.

I guess any herd is made up of some high-strung problem cows, some career cows who probably contribute the largest percentage of the farm's total production, and a third group, who, being new to this game, are trying to decide to which clique they should belong. I'll give them a hint – the career cows stay around longer, but the problem cows sure have more fun.

MAPS

One of the problems currently facing education is how to teach geography to the modern, hip, urbane, and sophisticated youth of today. Geography is just not exciting enough to keep the attention of our computer-literate, cell phone-using, video game junkie children.

This is where once again the agricultural industry can save the day. Farmers have the answer, especially those with cows. Many times the beautiful black blotches on Holstein cows are clearly in the shape of many of the earth's geographic features. Although not every cow has the map of a continent, ocean or U.S. state on its side, enough cows do to serve as very valuable, animated and living teaching aids.

Think of the fun children will have searching through hundreds of cows in hopes of finding a blotch in the shape of Florida, Hawaii or the Aleutian chain. Can't you see the excitement in their eyes when they find a cow with a perfect likeness of Wyoming on her side?

Some might say that using the markings on the sides of Holstein cows to teach geography to children is awkward, impractical and somewhat unpredictable. I contend that bringing cows with natural maps on their hides into the classroom is the ideal way to add zing to the otherwise dull subject of geography.

In addition, a white cow could be used to enliven classrooms with younger children by giving them black permanent markers and letting them draw their perception of a map of the United States, or even the world on the side of a cow.

At this point you are probably thinking, "Won't a live cow, loose in a classroom full of small children be somewhat disrupting?" Not necessarily, for cows, like people, enjoy a change of scenery once in a while. Just consider this little jaunt into academia as an ideal vacation for a cow and an invaluable learning experience for students.

DO COWS TALK?

Everyone knows that cows 'moo', but the deeper question is, "Do they actually talk?" If they talk, do they talk to each other or, for that matter, do they try to talk to anyone who will listen? I'm convinced that cows do talk. The problem is, we don't know what they are saying and most of the time neither do they.

Their moos can be divided into categories depending on their level of importance. The loudest is that of a mother for her calf. This constant ear-shattering bawling starts the second she is separated from her calf and continues until she completely forgets about her offspring, usually in less than three days. It is almost as if the act of giving birth strengthens her vocal cords.

The next bit of cow conversation to be explained is that of a cow experiencing the miracle of calf birth. As you might imagine, this is a very easily identified straining kind of groan not often heard by man because it usually occurs in the dark of the night.

Another readily recognizable moo is one general-purpose sound, appropriate for most occasions. I call it the 'beller', derived from the old English word bellow, which loosely translated means to make a noise like a cow. This beller is usually innocuous enough, except during special events such as the arrival of a new calf or a teenager stealing gas when every cow in the barn moos in unison. The resulting cacophony can wake even me from a sound sleep, convinced that the whole herd is about to burst into my bedroom and steal my teddy bear. The last time the intense amount of noise they made over a cow having a calf led me to the barn on a dead run with visions of cows running down the driveway, in the newly planted garden and, of course, splashing around in the swimming pool. My rule of thumb is, if they are bellowing, find out why. Cows are not like people, they only talk when they have something to say.

A trick some cows like to play on me is to hide amongst a group of cows and then start making noises that would lead me to believe that they need help. Then, when I go to investigate, they clam up, act innocent and pretend to be someone else just to confuse me.

From this dissertation on cows it is evident that cows communicate only in general terms. They are incapable of going into detail on anything, which is a good thing because their short attention span would make it hard for them to learn parts of speech or how to diagram a sentence.

To the inexperienced ear, all of the noises a cow makes sound alike. The reality is, a cow can delicately show concern, attract attention or even express sympathy just by how she talks or how she moos.

SMART COWS

When the technology of feeding a total mixed ration (TMR) came to dairy farms in this area, mixing all of the ingredients of a cow's daily ration together was found to be a great labor saver. Surprisingly, the cows eat more, give more milk, and have fewer digestive problems when fed TMR. Sounds like a win-win situation, doesn't it?

There is a downside. It is called a mixer wagon. This is the expensive, complicated, cumbersome device farmers use to mix together all of the forages, grains and minerals that make up a total mixed ration.

Mixer wagons fall into three categories: new, almost worn out and worn out. Because these essential machines are used to mix several loads every day of the year, they wear out quickly. Therefore, the best time to trade your old one in is just before it is ready for the scrap pile. If only we knew when that moment would be.

Mixer wagons do a great job of mixing all of the feeds into a ration that is so uniform that every bite a cow takes is exactly the same. That's the good news. The bad news is that my cows have been developing a way to unmix the mixed feed I provide for them, free of charge.

Cows have always preferred the grain portion of their diet to the roughages like corn and grass silage, much like I prefer jelly donuts and other carbohydrates to green beans and other vegetables. Sadly, I have learned that I must eat my salad in order to get dessert.

Anyway, a few of my cows have figured out how to separate the grain from the roughage, much the way kids always eat the center of Oreo cookies first. They do this by snorting while cleaning a spot in the bunk and very forcefully knocking some of the TMR into the cleared spot hard enough so that the grain falls from the roughage. They then snuffle up the separated grain with a sense of achievement and knock down some more feed. By doing this repeatedly, the cows sort out much of the grain, leaving silage for later, like eating dessert first.

Does this mean a dumb cow can outsmart a $25,000 mixer wagon? She can, she will, and she has!

THE COW AS A FOOD PROCESSOR

Every one of my cows eats over one hundred pounds of feed each and every day. From this she makes over 12 gallons of milk, 200 quarts of methane and what seems like a ton of manure. Sounds amazing, doesn't it? How do they do it? They can do it because a cow is the world's original food processor.

An electric food processor turns chunky stuff into mash by using a sharp stainless steel blade and making a lot of noise. A cow does the same thing just as efficiently without the use of electricity and making very little noise. The amazing thing is that she does all this without realizing she's doing it. In fact, she does nearly everything without realizing she's doing it!

Here's how she goes about it. She literally gobbles up everything that is put in front of her: silage, grain, and anything else the chopper picked up such as bits of plastic, balloons, kites, and pieces of errant soccer balls. This is all swallowed whole and goes directly into a huge vat called the rumen, where it is soaked in an icky soup full of bacteria, enzymes, and other interesting things with names too hard to spell. The rumen, full of odoriferous broth, is one of nature's miracles, having the ability to produce its own vitamins and turn nitrogen products into high quality proteins, all the while making growling noises.

Now here's the fun part. The cow processes this mess by regurgitating all the coarse materials in 'cuds' the size of your hand, thoroughly chewing each cud 71 times before swallowing the resultant mash, and sending it directly into the second, third, and finally the fourth stomach. Oh, I forgot to mention, cows are famous for having four stomachs. People only have one, although some of us look like we have four.

What happens after the fourth stomach I'll leave up to your imagination, but it is not pretty. At this point you are wondering where and when the milk making takes place. That's an udder story. Most people believe that all the milk a cow produces at each milking is carried in with her when she enters the milking parlor. That's not possible because most udders aren't big enough to hold the 50 pounds of milk or more she produces at each milking. Where does the milk come from? It's her little magic trick, for she actually produces half the milk she is going to give right there while the milker unit is clicking away. It's the other half she brings in with her.

As magical as the dairy cow is, don't expect her to pull any rabbits out of her horns, but she can make a lot of feed disappear.

COW ETIQUETTE

I know it is hard to believe, but cows adhere to a code of etiquette, just as some people do. This code is not obvious, nor has it ever been written down, probably because cows can't write.

The first rule seems to be: always treat your herd mates with kindness and courtesy. For example, we do not have free stalls enough for each cow to lie down in one, all at the same time. When all of the stalls are occupied and a standee wants to lie down, she has to convince one of her herd mates to get up and relinquish her precious stall. Very few cows are willing to give up a comfortable, well-bedded stall voluntarily. This is where etiquette comes in.

Cows are basically gentle creatures, as opposed to male cows. A bull would just go over to the occupant of his favorite stall and pound on her until she got up and ran away. Females, on the other hand, are more subtle. They use a more gentle technique.

Many times I have seen one cow, tired of standing, approach a cow lying in a freestall, and place her forehead firmly against the rump of the resting herd mate. First she pushes gently on her friend. If that doesn't work she gets more aggressive, pushing harder, then stopping, then pushing even harder, and stopping. In a few minutes she repeats this procedure. This gently approach is slow, but works well without destroying any friendships.

Another way cows are kind to each other is in the way they communicate with one another when they have an itch in a place they cannot scratch. On occasion I have witnessed one cow licking another cow's shoulder or back in a spot that they could not reach themselves. I have often wondered how the licker knew which spot to lick on the other cow. It must be a form of bovine mental telepathy unavailable to us lowly humans.

Cows are naturally herding animals, not comfortable unless in the company of others like themselves. They seem to blithely move as a group when being coaxed into the holding area or to another part of the barn. There is little crowding or pushing to see if you can get there first, like humans do at a rock concert and senior citizens do at a chicken barbecue.

Occasionally there are breeches of etiquette, as with any group of females, but I have never seen any hair pulling or temper tantrums and never once have I heard a cow say, "You just wouldn't understand."

Yes, cows are naturally polite animals. It is we humans who must polish our etiquette skills.

DO COWS EVER SLEEP?

"Do cows ever sleep?" I once asked my father over dinner one evening. My father was a calm and thoughtful man who always answered my questions carefully and in great detail. Sometimes I thought he was too deliberate and too detailed.

My mother once defended his painstakingly slow explanations by pointing out that a schoolteacher mother and an old maid aunt, both with a reputation for being persnickety perfectionists, had raised him. Mom felt that, in retaliation, he had developed the habit of using great care in the selection of each word. He seemed to be a font of knowledge on many subjects, but it took a lot of patience to extract any of it from him

Anyway, when I asked if cows ever slept soundly for hours at a time, oblivious to their surroundings, the way humans do, he immediately launched into a long explanation. He said that a cow's digestive system was actually made up of four stomachs, the first of which was a large vat of recently consumed feed, churning in a predigestive process that slowly and constantly releases methane gas. A cow regurgitates small portions of this partially digested food called cuds, thoroughly chewing and swallowing each cud again, before it passes into the second stomach.

The problem is that this methane gas is produced in large quantities all day and all night. Because of this continuous gas production and frequent burping with each cud that is chewed, a cow can't sleep for long periods of time or she would bloat from too much gas, shutting off the throat and resulting in death.

As logical as this explanation was, I still had to find out for myself if cows actually sleep. That's why one moonlit summer night I quietly slipped out of my bedroom while everyone else was sleeping and stealthily crept up to the pasture where our cows spent the night. Through the gloom I could see several prostrate bovines calmly chewing their cuds, oblivious to their surroundings. As I moved through the black and white forms not one sprawled-out, snoring, dead-to-the-world cow did I find.

In the 50 plus years since, I have seen many cows sleeping, but my father was right, they only sleep a few minutes at a time, between burps. However, in those few minutes when they are really sound asleep, they remind me of a sleeping dog, with their eyelids flicking and their feet twitching, as if they were dreaming of romping through a field of clover or finding an open gate. I just hope they enjoy their sleep as much as I do mine.

ATHLETIC TRAINERS

One day, while opening gates to let the cows back to eat after cleaning the barn, one huge, pregnant dry cow took advantage of my temporary lapse in protocol and darted through an open gateway and headed straight for the bunk full of fresh feed for the milk cows. Spotting her clandestine efforts to steal feed she wasn't entitled to, I tried to turn her around by waving my arms.

With a show of amazing dexterity and lightning quick reflexes, she started to go around to my right as I approached her. Then, to my amazement, she abruptly changed direction in mid-step and shot around to my left before I could recover enough to make an effort to stop her. Her reflexes were clearly faster than mine. How could a cow have such highly developed reflexes? How could an awkward, ungainly, 1,300 pound cow who takes ten minutes to gingerly leave the parlor so deftly avoid me? Could it be that my herd had been practicing how to outsmart me?

I was flabbergasted, disgusted, and a little humiliated. That cow moved faster than a defensive guard for the New York Knicks. That's when it struck me. With many team sports like soccer, basketball and football dependent on quick reaction speeds and with the increasing popularity of such sports world wide, new training methods to fine-tune a player's ability to speedily react are needed. Again, as in so other many crises, farm animals can come to the rescue.

That's right. I am proposing the use of cows to sharpen the reaction skills of athletes. Anyone who has tried to chase a herd of cows in an icy barnyard in the dark would recognize the wisdom of this innovative training method. Simply let a herd of cows loose and let the players try to steer, chase, cajole, and coax the cows back into a barn. Players would improve their running, blocking and leadership skills all at the same time.

This type of specialized training would be of great benefit to all athletes and, best of all, it wouldn't faze the cows at all. After all, it's the kind of activity they live for.

BOVINE BALLET STEPS

After returning from the ballet the other night, a neighbor commented on the agility of ballet dancers and I was reminded of the udder grace of the dairy cow. Just as ballet dancers have names for their dance steps, I have developed a similar terminology for the steps cows use in their everyday movements.

The most common is the 'switchback,' in which the nimble and clever bovine deludes the cow handler into thinking she will walk docilely in the direction you wish her to go. With this step the cow moves placidly in the appropriate direction, and then, without warning, she stops, spins around and runs right past you in the opposite direction. I am convinced that she would run between my legs if she thought she could get away with it. A variation of this movement is the 'double switchback' in which the cow dives behind another cow, hoping you won't notice that she is going the opposite way. This feat often takes place with such quickness and poise that the cow is successful in her ploy.

Probably the most recognizable ballet movement of cows is called 'derriere premiere' or 'backing up.' This is done either very slowly or so fast that you barely can get out of the way. Although not a particularly subtle maneuver, backing up has a certain elegance all its own. It occurs when a cow determines that the alley, lane or parlor she has entered is obviously not a good place to be, and she would rather retreat to the point where the mistake was made. The more intricate version of this move, the 'derriere pas de tout', takes place when a cow tries to avoid coming into the parlor, or when she attempts to come back into the parlor from the exit door in order to check on things and then has to back out and step down at the same time.

Of course, cows don't require special expensive satin ballet slippers to stand on their tiptoes. The only time that cows do appear to stand on point is when they are trying to steal something that they shouldn't have that was purposely put up high, such as a glass thermometer, a can of spray paint, or a tuna sandwich.

Ballet dancers routinely stand on one foot and spin around while gracefully waving their arms. A cow rarely does this. The only time I saw it happen was not a pretty sight. And while dancers can rise from a prone position with ease and beauty, my cows need a lesson in rising without lunging.

The only other ballet-like step that my cows perform looks very much like a 'kick'. Much like ballet, there are five basic kicks, all performed in the parlor. The first kick is done solely for the purpose of getting your attention. The second kick involves stepping on the milker hose, while the third kick requires dexterity and timing to inflict maximum pain to the farmer's elbow. The fourth kick, if done properly, completely removes the milker unit from the udder in one smooth swift motion. And the fifth and final kick is reserved for first calf heifers who have yet to learn that being milked, or not, isn't a choice they are allowed make.

I hope this analysis helps you better appreciate the dance steps cows do naturally, without any training or discipline.

And when people suggest that only ballet dancers are agile - point them to the pastures for a divinely bovine cultural experience!

Chapter 5

MILK HAULERS

One of the many unsung heroes of modern agriculture is the milk hauler. Somewhere between the cow and the cheese on your pizza is the person responsible for daily moving tons of milk hundreds of miles in weather conditions that would close schools and force skiers indoors.

Most milk today is hauled long distances directly from the farm to large efficient milk plants. This is done with a large tractor-trailer often referred to as a 'semi'. Of course, semi means half and these trucks are referred to this way because they are only half as much fun to drive as a car.

Picture yourself sitting behind the wheel of a monster almost as long as a football field that weighs 15 tons empty and over 45 tons loaded. Then drive this thing at speeds up to 60 miles an hour through a maize of tiny automobiles whose drivers think you can stop as easily as they can.

Now, let's add the handicap of not being able to see what is beside you on either side when making even the slightest turn. I hope by now you're beginning to understand how difficult it is to drive a semi. Think how difficult it must be in times of poor visibility or when the 'dispatcher' has just chewed you out for being behind schedule. Then there is the added challenge offered by the obstacle course layouts of farm driveways. Most farmsteads were designed well before the advent of semi trucks. Therefore, most require the hauler to back up to the milk house door at odd angles, up hills or between precariously laid out mazes of calf hutches, parked tractors and blind cats.

That's all there is to it, except for the constant threat of the NYS Department of Transportation and several levels of law enforcement that could ground your perishable load at any moment.

And then there is the amazing range of attitudes of the many drivers I have met. Some are 'Nervous Nellies', constantly fretting, stewing and complaining about their trucks, their jobs and their bosses. Others are not overly concerned about any of the daily obstacles they face. Most make this awesome responsibility look as easy as a car trip to the mall.

It's not a job for the faint of heart. I'm just glad there is always an unsung hero to take my milk to market everyday.

SALES PEOPLE

Like it or not, farmers have to depend on sales people for much of the supplies they need to keep their farms running smoothly, not to mention an unending supply of note pads, pens and those ubiquitous hats. A salesperson can be someone you hide from when you see them coming, or they can be your friend who offers good advice from knowledge gained by watching the messes others have gotten themselves into on the countless farms they visit.

Although you may think sales calls are annoying, there are benefits. For instance, a salesman can also be a great source of gossip. Farmers are never too busy to hear about the latest mistake, miscalculation or misfortune of others. And, a discreet salesperson will not mention any names, giving you confidence that they will not go around revealing any of your really dumb mistakes, like the time I forgot to check the wheel nuts and the rear tractor tire fell right off. But I like the salesmen who have no scruples and show no hesitation in extolling all the gory details of someone else's humiliating experience.

If sales people are good they will be so convincing that you won't be able to live without their product or service. If they are not, we hate to see them coming, laugh about them at barbecues, and warn others about them. If they are good, they will respect your time as valuable and not take too much of it. If they are not, you may have to fake a heart attack just to get rid of them.

I was a sales person once, so I know all the tricks people use to avoid talking to one - everything from abruptly turning and walking away in the middle of my sales talk, to staging a disappearing act as my car rolls to a stop in their dooryard.

You may think sales is the easiest job in the world. Just ride around all day without having to do a lick of work, talking to people and spreading anonymous gossip. If you think it's that easy, just try it yourself sometime. You never hear about the endless paperwork, impossible quotas, and intimidating sales managers. On the other hand, you will learn to talk fast, you will become good at playing hide and seek and you will always have a clean hat to wear.

RECYCLING

We all think that recycling is a new concept invented in the late twentieth century by those concerned with the future of our environment. In reality, recycling is not a new concept at all.

For example, our big farmhouse, as best we can tell, was built nearly 200 years ago. The first floor stringers, visible from the basement, have occasional mortises cut into them, with no tenons inserted. It is obvious that these beams came from another building, so even at that time recycling was in vogue. I can picture those early homebuilders sorting through a pile of used timbers trying to find a few they could use for their current project. Of course, in those days everything was made from something else. Nothing was ever thrown away or worse yet, burned or discarded.

This same frugality was apparent in our ancestors' judicious use of flat rocks. Before the invention or accidental discovery of cement, all foundations in our area were dependent on someone carefully constructing a cellar wall made entirely of flat fieldstones. Some were fresh from the earth while others were recycled from stonewalls between fields or from old foundations.

The recycling of rocks has a long history. Many stones from the walls of abandoned abbeys in England have shown up in stone buildings on farmsteads and in villages all over that country. And even tombstones have been used as sidewalks. That's the thing about those flat rocks – they will go on and on. Today's old foundations, long after the barn has fallen in or burned, will become tomorrow's wall around a flower garden, terraced lawn, or as a last resort, an above-ground pool.

The secret of recycling is finding homes for things we no longer use. Those empty milk replacer bags could see new life as ghost costumes for kindergarten children or be left at discount super markets for those who forget to bring their own bags. Old bathtubs could be sold to those wishing to build lawn shrines. Old tires could go rolling on as all-season sandboxes, seats on swing sets, or decorations on trench silos.

If you have too much of anything, there has to be a way to recycle it. Get those creative juices flowing! See if you can be more creative than your ancestors were.

THE JOB INTERVIEW

Much has been written about job interviews. These stories are full of tips on how to convince a prospective employer that you are the best one for the job. Unfortunately, very little has been written about how an employer can determine, from one short, tension-filled interview, if a person has the qualities necessary for the job.

Well, all you prospective employers out there can relax, for I have found the perfect way to evaluate many of the qualities you are seeking in the people you hire. This method is amazing in its simplicity, efficient in its timing and unswerving in its accuracy. Are you ready for this?

Simply offer to go grocery shopping with your prospective employee. Then, watch closely how he goes about such a simple task. Why? Because, as a wise person once said, "You can learn a lot just by watching."

First, do they have a shopping list? If not, they may not be well organized. As they shop, take note of the items they select. If they choose store brands over more expensive name brands, they are able to determine value. However, if they choose too many gourmet items, they may tend to be extravagant. If they load up on prepared foods rather than the basics, they may not be the best financial managers. Likewise, too much junk food in their shopping carts could indicate a tendency to be compulsive decision-makers. And, if they plan their trip through the store such that highly perishable items like ice cream are selected last, they have the ability to prioritize.

But the real test of a person's abilities occurs at the checkout counter. Do they group their items, for example, place all frozen items together? Are produce, boxes and jars grouped to make bagging easier and storing food at home simpler? This is where you will find out if a person can stay well organized under pressure. Do they have their money, credit card or checkbook out, with the check signed and dated? Do they do their own bagging or do they wait for someone else to do it for them? How do they react as the bagger squeezes one more six pound can of coffee on top of the bag holding the bread and rolls? Do they exhibit agitation as the credit card machine acts up or the two-year-old waiting in line behind them knocks the candy rack over?

You get the idea. During an interview a person can tell you anything. A resume may be the greatest piece of fiction you will ever read. Only by grocery shopping with someone, will you ever learn what he or she is really like.

ODE TO A TRACTOR

Some have said you were only a tractor.
    Such a callous, brutal understatement offends me.
For your dedication and loyalty alone
    Hath left a warm spot in my heart forever.
I knew from the day I saw you at the auction
    We were meant for each other.
As the bidding started I held my breath,
    Hoping that no one wanted you more than I.
When the auctioneer, with one stroke of his gavel,
    Pointed to me and shouted, "Sold,"
I felt my prayers were answered.

You didn't disappoint me.
    You were more than I expected.
The older tractors at home would be pleased I thought,
    For they had been working hard, too hard for their age.

Bursting with pride I drove you all the way home,
    Right through town, my head held high.
Once home I treated you to an oil and filter change,
    A new seat and even a new muffler.
Nothing was too good for my John Deere 4020,
    The flagship of my fledgling fleet.

At first, we did everything together:
    Manure spreading, plowing, disking, and chopping.
However after a few years your age began to show.
    At first it was a clutch, then a complete motor job.
Later came the new tires.
    Through it all you never complained,
Always starting on the first spin, always anxious to please.
    I could tell you worked hard for your previous owner.
Why had he abandoned you?
    Perhaps for something newer, flashier, with a heated and
       air-conditioned cab?

For may years you were the only one who mightily pulled
    Hundreds of loads of silage onto our trenches.
The only one to pull the manure spreader
    Through the deep snow blanketing our cornfields.
The only one to come to the rescue of stuck mailmen,
    Spinning lime trucks and sliding milk tankers.
Over the years I can only remember
    Two engine overhauls and three new clutches.

Only one bad mud incident sticks in my mind
    And that wasn't your fault.
The spring must have been wetter than usual
    And the spot looked deceivingly dry.
Alas, once you sank, the mud hole seemed bottomless.
    I thought we would never get you out.

We pulled, we pushed, we yanked,
  And we even tried two tractors,
But the mud's suction was too much.
  As I remember, we left you for a few days
To let the sun use its natural drying powers.
  The experience taught us to be more careful,
To not ask you to go where we knew you should not go.

I never tired of sitting on your yellow vinyl seat,
  All of the vital levers at my fingertips.
Watching your tachometer needle rise and fall
  And the black smoke pour from your muffler
As we plowed, disked and chopped our way
  through the long days.

At last the time came when we needed a bigger tractor.
  There was too much to till, to plant and to harvest
And so little time to do it all.
  Then the opportunity appeared.
A late model four-wheel drive with, yes,
  A sound guard cab, heat and air,
And it only needed some mechanical repairs.
  This was too good an opportunity to pass up.
At last we would no longer fear those wet spring days
  When daily spreading was a challenge.

But to make this wonderful acquisition possible,
    We would have to trade in one of our present tractors.
The most valuable to trade and least needed,
    after the 4-wheel drive acquisition was,
I'm sad to say, our trusted and loyal 4020.
    It was not an easy decision.
It was a good deal, we needed a bigger tractor,
    And it would speed up our planting and harvesting.

I was sad the day you left the farm,
    Chained to a rollback truck.
I watched as the truck got smaller and smaller
    and eventually disappeared.
I heard that your new owner took you to some tractor pulls.
    I am sure you did your best.
I hope you are allowed to spend your remaining days
    On a small farm somewhere,
Raking and baling hay and giving an occasional hayride,
    but mostly just resting.
No matter where you are,
    You will always be in my heart.
I will always think of you as my 4020.

PERSONAL AD

Although I am happily married, I am still fascinated by the personal ads in our weekly paper. I can't help but notice that the ads are very short and require a great deal of thought to be worded enticingly enough for someone to respond. Talk about marketing!

Some words appear frequently and could be a secret code. When they say full-figured, anorexia apparently is not a problem. When men say they like cats, they must be desperate. Women love cats, men only tolerate them. Many of those placing ads describe themselves as humorous. I'm not sure if that is interchangeable with laughable, but they must figure a sense of humor would be attractive to the opposite sex.

If a farmer were to place a personal ad seeking female companionship it might read: Full figured SM dairy farmer who enjoys talking about cows, going for long walks to check on crops and attending farm auctions seeks SF who enjoys cooking, especially lasagna and fried chicken, quiet evenings in the barn and chasing heifers. Experience with jumper cables and duct tape a plus. Must have own jackknife. A lasting relationship with this caring farmer is possible for the right person, if they can feed calves, pack trench and teach him to use a computer.

This ad might read differently if it were placed by a farm woman seeking a companion. The theme would be the same but the emphasis would be in different areas.

Such an ad might read: Hands on, confident, take charge SF capable of dehorning a cow, rebuilding a diesel engine and designing a website who enjoys growing zucchini, making rope halters and listening to weather reports, is seeking SM farmer with good loamy soil and a registered herd, who enjoys garage sales, church suppers and garden tours. Good hygiene a must, should be good with cows, children and cats. Must be willing to ask directions, leave boots at the door, milk early on bingo nights and be on time for meals.

Of course, single farmers rarely see ads like that one. Rather they read an ad such as: slender and demure SF who enjoys nights out, having her nails done and talking on the phone seeks SM companion for expensive dinners, weekend flings in Paris and skiing in Vail. Must enjoy long romantic walks, small fluffy dogs and white carpets. It is the young hopeful dairy farmer that sees this as a challenge, and really believes that this diva could embrace farm life.

Now that I think about it, I am very lucky that the SF home economist that I met in college and wooed into marrying me came to enjoy canning, gardening, doing farm books, having brown carpets and packing trench. She still isn't good with jumper cables, but makes up for it with her to-die-for rhubarb pie.

MY MILK TRUCK DRIVERS

Farmers will always be dependent on many wonderful people to provide them with the services necessary to operate a modern farm. One of the most important, but least appreciated, is the milk truck driver. While farmers spend all day in one place, milk truck drivers never spend a single day in one place. With their truck as their steed, they ride from farm to farm, gathering their load. No one do we see more often nor take for granted as much as our milk truck driver.

Over the years I've gotten to know a wide spectrum of personalities and moods in the milk transport specialists who daily visit my cluttered milk house. Some of them are cheerful and brighten my day. Others are consummate pessimists who see each molehill as a mountain. Some are able to back from the road into our short driveway in one smooth motion and stop precisely at our milk house door. Others have to make several 'forward and backs' to make the long trailer go the way they want it to. The short piece of decorative split rail fence beside the driveway has nearly been backed over several times. Many drivers have stayed on my route for a few years, others only a few months, moving on to driving jobs less demanding or better paying.

Treasured are the cheerful optimists who see a freezing rain as a challenge and a reminder of how easy most of the year will be. As for the short-tempered, down personalities, I just tolerate them for they won't be around long. It's too demanding a profession for those with bad tempers and lack of judgment.

Sometimes I can be of help to the young fellows just starting out in this difficult world of milk movement. For example, one young Lothario was lamenting his confusion at how to act on his first date with a girl he just met. He said, "All she wanted to do was talk, talk, talk. I hardly had a chance to say anything."

At last I had a chance to share some of my hard-earned human relations skills, accumulated over a lifetime of mistakes, missteps, and humiliating blunders. I advised him in a fatherly fashion that the amazing secret for men to get along well with women is simply to be a good listener. An occasional nod of agreement is all that is necessary. And, the best part is, you don't actually have to listen; just pretending to listen is all that is needed. Everyone loves a good listener.

He thanked me for my advice and left with a better understanding of how to impress the opposite sex. I never heard how his next date went, as he was fired soon after for backing into someone's milk house and not telling anyone. I have always wondered if my advice helped or hindered his love life.

OVERHEARD IN THE BARN

You would be surprised at the things one can learn in the barn. Here are some of the funniest things that I have said or overheard:

"Gosh Doc. Are you all right? I don't know what got into her. She's never kicked like that before. Boy, I bet that really hurts!"

My parts man always says, "I never saw one like that before."

"Don't worry so much. Just remember, it's always darkest just before you step on the cat."

"What we really need is a high-yielding weed you can't kill which is rich in protein."

"My barn clothes really need washing. There's not much fabric left as they are mostly manure and hydraulic oil."

"Anyone who thinks marriage is a 50:50 proposition either doesn't understand women or fractions."

"Why is a glass of beer at two dollars perfectly acceptable while a glass of milk for 75 cents is inflationary?"

"I came from a poor family. We didn't have too much and that's a tradition I am passing on to my kids."

"The check is in the mail."

"With these low interest rates, today it's a real bargain to be in debt."

"If you think no one notices how you look, try cutting your own hair."

"It seems like no matter how busy some people are, they are never too busy to stop and talk about how busy they are."

"It always rains after a dry spell."

"One word of advice: never plant a garden larger than your wife can care for."

They say getting old makes you think more about the here-after. I certainly do. No matter where I go I have to ask myself, "Now, what am I here after?"

"Don't worry, if everything goes right I should be done milking and down to the house by seven."

"I'm almost done. I'll be down in just a few minutes."

"I know I said seven, but..."

"O.K. If that's the way you feel, go without me!"

WORKING ON A FARM

Working on a farm is such wonderful preparation for life. If only everyone could experience the incredible opportunity for growing, learning and sweating that summer on a dairy farm offers.

There are so many skills that one picks up from spending the summer on a farm. One quickly becomes adept at removing an upside down and rather confused cow from a feed bunk, raking a perfect windrow, and pounding the dents out of the tractor hood in mere seconds before the boss returns from the fair.

Yes, there are many invaluable lessons to be learned by working on a farm. For example, my young helper recently learned a timeless lesson when he ran out of fuel while haying on rented land three miles from our farm. Imagine the sinking feeling he must have felt as the sky darkened with threatening storm clouds and the tractor suddenly sputtered and lurched to a stop. He was lucky to find someone home at the first house he approached, only a long hot walk from the field.

By the time we arrived with more fuel, the raindrops were beginning to descend. I patiently explained the importance of always knowing how much fuel your tractor contains before you start out on a project, especially one that is far from home. You can be sure that this high school senior, an aspiring helicopter pilot, will always check the fuel level in his machines before taking off.

I'll bet that his future employers, fellow pilots, and young wife will always be grateful for the lessons he learned on the farm. In fact, the experience of working on a farm is so valuable that it really should be mandatory in most high school and college curricula. This would both better prepare the nation's youth for the rigors of life and solve the labor shortage on most farms. What a great benefit for all involved. The only question is: Do the nation's farmers have enough patience to cope with a new crop of students each year?

BECOMING COMPUTER LITERATE

I recently completed an adult education course entitled, "Becoming Computer Literate." It must have been successful for now I can confidently sit down at any personal computer and, with a few deft clicks of a mouse, erase everything on its hard drive, order things I can neither pay for nor want to get caught reading, and accidentally order a five year supply of lifestyle enhancing drugs.

This course taught me how truly intelligent these buggers really are. They don't miss a thing. For example, in the lesson on how easy it is to use the Internet, the instructor had each of us apply for our own e-mail account. In filling out the application online I must have inadvertently entered the current date in the space meant for my birth date. The computer was sharp enough to catch that mistake. It immediately detected that I was a minor and therefore I could not get an e-mail account without my parents' permission and would I please enter my parents e-mail address so that parental permission could be obtained. Being over 60 with both parents deceased for over 30 years, I had no choice but to raise my hand and ask, "What do I do now?" A quick review of my application revealed my error.

One thing I learned about computers is that they are best at storing and retrieving large amounts of information quickly. On the farm this could be helpful with breeding, production and financial records. The only problem is that you have to put the information into the computer first.

The down side is that computers, more than most farm tools, are apt to break down, catch fire or come down with a virus. To aid us, the instructor handed out a list of 'Do's and Don'ts' for computers. The most obvious 'Do' said, "If you can't live without a computer for any length of time, get a second computer." A 'Don't' was the same advice that my wife gave me, "Don't talk to or accept e-mail from strangers."

The most obvious 'Don't' advised, "Don't throw away the box your computer came in, in case you need to ship it back. At least keep it for the length of the warranty period." Apparently if it doesn't break while still under warranty, when it does break, it will be too obsolete to be repaired. Oh, I also learned to always unplug your personal computer during thunderstorms and power outages, or you will soon be searching for the box it came in.

Well, that's it. These were the high points of how to become computer literate. Now you can go and erase your own hard drive.

Chapter 6

SHUT DOWN

Have you ever climbed into a vehicle and turned on the ignition only to have the radio suddenly come on full blast, the windshield wipers flail madly and the air conditioning fan blast in your face? After you regain your composure and try to recall why you were there in the first place, to say, "I hate it when that happens!" seems an understatement.

My lecture on "How to Shut Off a Vehicle," is legendary, just ask anyone in my family. My premise is to treat every motorized conveyance as you would an airliner and simply shut it down in a predetermined sequence.

Take my big tractor, for instance. After working it hard, it takes several steps to properly shut it off. First, the engine must be brought back to an idle so the turbo-charger can be properly cooled and lubricated. Then the radio and air-conditioning fan must be turned off. Next, the shift lever must be put in neutral and the range lever pulled into the park position. Then, and only then, can the engine be killed by pulling the 'stop' cable plunger all the way out. At this point the ignition can be turned off. Next, the following questions must be answered.

Are all the lights turned off? Are all hydraulic implements lowered to the ground? Have you taken your thermos and what's left of your lunch with you? It is important at this point to be sure to take your hidden store of M&M's, lest the next driver find and eat them. If you have answered all these questions in the affirmative, and nothing has exploded, then, at last, you may exit the cab. This procedure may sound complicated but a similar checklist may be applied to any vehicle.

Whenever I pass the open cockpit door on an airliner and catch a glimpse of all those gauges, dials and switches, I can't help but think, "That pilot may be able to fly a 747, but I'll bet he doesn't know how to shut down a John Deere 4250." I wonder where he keeps his M&M's.

WHAT IS AUTO STEERING?

With all the modern conveniences available on tractors today, it is inevitable that some computer nerd, with too much time on his hands, will perfect a way for a satellite to steer your tractor for you. As if it is hard work to steer a tractor while sitting in a plush chair inside a glass-enclosed, air-conditioned cab, listening to a stereo.

If someone or something did the steering for you, what would keep you from dozing off and chisel plowing right across someone's lawn? Not that it hasn't happened to me before, and I didn't need any help from a satellite either!

According to the ads, these automatic steering systems are guaranteed to give you hands-free, straight-line steering while automatically adjusting ground speed to achieve optimal efficiency. Now who wouldn't want to be optimally efficient while taking a nap at the same time?

These auto-steer systems might work in the mile square fields of the Midwest, but with our little odd-shaped, horizontally-challenged, postage stamp-sized fields in the northeast, we would spend more time fixing the system's broken wires and blown fuses than actually using them.

The only time I wished I had someone watching me from above was once, early in my farming career. With only 30 cows and barely 100 acres of crops, I was pinching every penny. A six-acre field needed lime and, after shopping around, I ordered a load from the lowest cost vendor. When he arrived in an old truck with few windows intact, I knew how he kept his costs down. As was the custom, I climbed in the truck to ride along to be sure that he found the correct field. It was long and narrow, surrounded by a hedgerow of bushes and mature trees.

The lime must have come from a pile that was very dry, for when he threw the bed chain and spinners in gear and floored the old truck, we were immediately engulfed in a dense cloud of dust. It was as if we were in an airliner descending through a layer of clouds. As the engine roared and the lime flew, I heard the driver say, "How far up ahead do you think the hedgerow is?"

Boy, if there ever was a time I needed a satellite to tell me where I was, that was it!

EMERGENCY CALL

It seldom happens, but my son and I each had the same night off last week. He and his wife were at the comedy club while I was spending my free night at the grocery store. I was trying to find all the lost leaders when my cell phone rang. It seems the gate to the push off had been carelessly left open and a cow had fallen into the manure spreader parked beneath. I could have forgotten the cell phone or even turned it off, but, no, I always carried it with me just in case I was needed.

I was needed all right! To my son's dismay, we agreed that both of us would have to come home to rescue this damsel in distress. When I got there and peered down into the huge V-shaped spreader, my eyes met those of a scared, confused and helpless first calf heifer whose rump was firmly wedged in the spreader. By then my son had arrived and, with our new hired hand, we quickly developed a plan of action. Someone would connect a chain to the cow while I got the tractor with the front-end loader on it. That way I stayed clean. While others were attaching the chain to the cow I removed the muffler and air cleaner from the tractor so they would not hit the low ceiling by the push off.

When everyone was ready and the chain was carefully in place, I raised the loader and backed up at the same time. The dazed animal slid onto the push-off floor like a freshly landed fish, but more fragrant.

Once the chain was removed and she had a short rest, the heifer scampered to her feet and walked off toward the feed bunk as if nothing had happened. Something had happened to her though. She had a narrow escape and was covered with a thick veneer of manure.

When accidents such as this happen, it is fortunate that they usually happen to young, healthy and vigorous animals who recover quickly. That's because the young ones are the curious inexperienced types, always snooping around looking for something to get into. Old cows are lying down, eating, or chewing their cud, too busy to get into trouble. Come to think of it, the same holds true for people.

Thank goodness for some quick thinking and my trusty bucket loader. Guess my son didn't need a night off to find something to laugh about.

BATTLING HEDGEROWS

Hedgerows are nature's way of making you slow down. They didn't always exist. First the land was cleared and fences built. Immediately trees and brush began to grow up in the fence lines. Birds added their contributions by depositing cherry pits and other seeds while resting on the fences. These narrow strips of tangled bushes and trees suddenly took on a life of their own. Wild grapevines climbed to the tops of the tallest trees. Other fast growing species rapidly filled in the spaces between the trees with a dense wall of foliage so impenetrable that sneaking a peek of the neighbor's crops or wife sunbathing was almost impossible.

Since we no longer pasture our cattle we have removed most of the hedgerows on our farm. All that remain are those along the perimeter of our land, but their prolific growth continues to drive me crazy. Why trees and weeds grow so profusely along property lines is one of life's great mysteries.

I have been working to contain one hedgerow for over 40 years now. Each time I cut off the protruding limbs of any problem trees and chop down all the sumac, everything starts to grow back within a few days. In fact, sumac grows so fast that I have learned never to turn my back on it. I have known sumac to reach heights of six feet in the time it takes me to eat lunch. My wife tried to tell me I had just returned to a different field, but I know better. I never did trust the darned stuff. Anything with such bright red leaves in the fall surely has been up to no good.

Unfortunately, today's fast-paced farming does not let you slow down. In dealing with hedgerows, you really have only three choices. The easiest is to give in to their evil powers and forget about them entirely. Of course, this means that eventually the forest will reclaim all of the land. Secondly, you could adopt a scorched earth policy, using flame-throwers and dynamite to remove the noxious hedgerows. But perhaps the best solution is to rent the hedgerows out to some professional overachiever who wishes he had a little piece of the country and let him try to tame a hedgerow. It might help him slow down, too.

FOOTBATHS

You think your feet are tired after a long day? Be happy that you're not a cow. You see cows are plagued with many foot problems, perhaps because they walk around in the muck all day or simply because each foot alone must hold up over 300 pounds of cow. On top of that, a new foot problem has recently appeared on dairy farms called 'hairy foot warts'. It turns out these so-called warts neither have hair nor are a true wart, but once named by the experts, no one has the nerve to call them what they really are: 'pesky little white sore spots that won't go away'.

Whereas we might take our tired little doggies to the beauty parlor for a pedicure, it isn't easy to find a parlor servicing bovines, no matter how trendy and picturesque it might seem. The best treatment the pros have come up with for treating 'hairy foot warts' is to have all of your cows walk through a four inch deep trough of water mixed with whatever medication they are selling that day. This is called a footbath. I am sure the cows call it something else.

It is not really a bath. After all, who would ever attempt to give each cow a bath everyday, or even once a week, even for medicinal purposes. All we want to bathe is their feet.

Our footbath is a tray three feet wide, six feet long and four inches deep. We put it by the parlor exit door so the cows must walk through it as they leave the parlor and most of them do, albeit reluctantly.

However, every herd has a few cows that seem determined to do anything to avoid stepping directly into the footbath. Some try to jump entirely over it. This usually results in a big splash that coats me, the walls, and any stray salesmen with the preparation of the day. Some cows are more graceful and try to walk along the edges of the tray without actually getting their feet wet. But the most clever and perhaps overly cautious cattle try to avoid the footbath completely by turning around to go back into the parlor, only to be pushed backend first through the footbath and out the door by the cows that were following her.

After all this trouble, our cows still have hairy warts, but the parlor walls and I seem to be wart free. Hmm, I wonder if I could develop a footbath to reduce other common annoyances, such as unwanted pounds from excess calories.

HAMMERS

A good hammer is like a good friend, always there when you need them. Both should be unobtrusive, reliable, and exude a calm confidence.

We have lots of hammers: brass hammers, ball peen hammers, sledge hammers, claw hammers, dead blow hammers, blacksmith hammers and, of course, tack hammers.

Each was designed for a specific purpose and should never be used for anything else. That's in an ideal world, of course. Unfortunately, we don't live in an ideal world.

On most farms, when a hammer is needed, anything heavy, within arms reach, will do. It is best if this object is neither brittle nor expensive. We have found from experience that an adjustable wrench works almost as well as a hammer for many jobs. Maybe it should be called an 'adjustable hammer'. Also, it is important to choose the right size hammer for the task, because the bigger the hammer you start with, the sooner you will have to go to town for parts.

The least valuable hammers on our farm are referred to as 'toolbox hammers'. Every tractor toolbox has one. Its sole responsibility is to drive hitch pins out. Occasionally it will be used to straighten something that is bent or to assist in some minor repair or adjustment. When that happens it will inevitably be left laying on the plow or disk frame and be promptly plowed under, never to surface again for centuries until some future archeologist comes across it in a futile search for Indian arrowheads. Because of their short working life, toolbox hammers need not be finely crafted machine tools. Anything priced under two dollars at a garage sale will do, even ball peen hammers with chunks chipped off their faces and carpenter hammers with only one claw. As long as it has a handle connected to a head of some kind, any kind, it will qualify as a toolbox hammer.

It is quite a blow to lose a friend or a hammer. The only way to keep either is to take better care of them.

PLOWING

Farmers love to plow. Every spring they can't wait to get out into the field, turn over that rich soil and watch it crumble as it turns and flows off the end of the moldboard. It gives farmers a sense of purpose. It's an "at last I am doing something constructive" feeling after a winter of carrying feed to and manure away from those ubiquitous bovines.

Words cannot describe the glorious feeling of hearing the sound of a diesel engine working hard, inhaling the odor of unburned diesel fuel emanating from the plumes of black smoke hovering overhead and seeing the six-foot swath of dark soil unwinding behind. Think of it, you are sitting on a comfortable padded seat in an air-conditioned cab listening to your favorite radio station, in command of all you survey.

Other than your cell phone, you are insulated from the cares of the world. It just doesn't get any better than this. A word of caution is appropriate here: don't shut off your phone for you never know when a tire will go flat, an oil line will burst or your radio will go dead. Having a cell phone with you could save a long walk through a muddy field.

Farmers also love to plow because it awakens their primal instincts to play in the dirt. As little kids, farmers spent many happy hours making 'vroom vroom' noises while piling dirt into trucks with toy pay loaders, dumping those loads and smoothing them out with die-cast metal tractors and harrows, while dreaming of the day they would be driving back and forth, tilling the soil like real farmers do. With luck this earth-moving project did not disrupt mother's freshly planted garden.

But this wonderful picture is threatened by a changing world. It seems that the new philosophy is to till the soil less or not at all. This minimum or no-till practice is better for the soil but not for a farmers' psyche. Minimum till is done with a chisel plow, which tills the soil while leaving enough organic matter on the surface to prevent erosion. It isn't nearly as much fun as the faithful old moldboard plow.

The no-till planter is even better for the soil, but a real ego crusher. For one thing, when you look back, you can't tell where you have been. For another, everything is done in one pass, eliminating hours of riding around in air-conditioned, stereo-listening comfort. What fun is that? The time saved will probably be spent fixing fence, cutting brush or worse yet, milking cows.

Sometimes progress is a good thing, but in this case, I'm not so sure.

GREAT ADVENTURE

We don't use our big tractor at all during the winter. For the winter months it hibernates secure in quiet slumber in the back corner of our tool shed. When the snow is gone and the grass is not yet green we awaken it and drive it into our farm shop to prepare it for the spring planting season.

This year as I brought the beast to life I was reminded of the story of the farmer who, like me, hurriedly climbed into the cab of his long-sleeping favorite tractor, started it up and began maneuvering it out into the spring sunshine.

The cab of a tractor, even an inactive one, is a safe secure place during a long winter. That's why it is not uncommon for a mouse to build a nest under a tractor seat and not be disturbed. One must pound their fist on the seat each spring to dislodge any uninvited guests. I always do.

This fellow didn't so as he was carefully squeezing between the haybine and the field chopper, a mouse, disturbed by all the noise, ran out from under the tractor seat, made two laps around the floor of the cab, and, seeing no other means of escape, mistook the loose leg of a coverall for a hole to hide in. That's right, this rudely awakened wild mouse ran up the unsuspecting farmer's pant leg in a vain attempt to reach freedom.

What would you do if a mouse ran up your pant leg while you were driving a huge machine through a tight space? Of course the farmer panicked and started pounding his leg, hoping to stop the mouse's progress, ignoring the direction the tractor was going. When he finally looked up he had driven through his wife's garden, across the lawn and was headed for the road. Fortunately he stopped before the school bus whizzed by.

His close call was the talk of the neighborhood. Those tire tracks were visible from the road, so for the next few weeks he had to explain why he drove through three fences, a lawn and a garden for no apparent reason. He got the mouse though, which was all that really mattered.

This year when I get the big tractor out, I'll be sure to pound on the seat first so this won't happen to me.

THE SCOOP ON SKID STEERS

Not many people know the history behind the invention of the skid steer, that ubiquitous little self-propelled loader that can spin itself in a complete circle within its own length and seemingly do almost anything except climb stairs and turn somersaults.

These contraptions are called skid steers because they literally steer by skidding their tires. They have no other steering mechanism whatsoever. This intriguing concept was invented by a farmer when the steering apparatus on his small loader broke and, out of necessity, he found he could still maneuver his loader by simply pushing the individual brakes on each wheel and letting one side push the other side around. This is one time when it is acceptable to spin your wheels.

When his innovation was discovered, skid steers began turning up on farms all over America. In fact, they became so common for so many uses on so many farms that a new phenomenon appeared. It seems that these harmless little machines, if left alone, sometimes have a mind of their own.

On some farms, where skid steers are used for barn cleaning and other utility chores, farmers have noticed a fair bit of damage caused by these machines. It starts out innocently enough. A chipped curb here, a broken post there, and an occasional broken light fixture. This kind of skid steer inflicted damage is known in the trade as 'skid steer blight'. If you ask anyone who operates these machines about this 'blight', they don't seem to know when or how this damage occurred. The only explanation seems to be that the skid steer must have done it all by itself, when no one was around. Can't you just picture the skid steer do-si-do-ing down the alley, inadvertently bouncing off waterers, stalls and curbs?

What can be done about this? I suggest having a serious heart to heart talk with your skid steer, pointing out how expensive and time-consuming it is to repair this havoc and emphasizing that everyone and every machine on the farm must work as a team. Let me know if this advice works. It hasn't for me, but then again, my skid steer is really stubborn.

ELECTRICITY

There is no doubt about it; modern efficient dairy farms would not be possible without electricity. Yes, this cheap, silent and abundant source of energy milks our cows, cools our milk and performs thousands of other jobs around the farm.

Although nowadays we take the modern milking machine, silo unloader and hot water heater for granted, 100 years ago farmers did not have any of these labor saving devices. And it is just as well, because they didn't have any place to plug them in.

To help you understand how electricity works, let's look at the simple electric circuit. The electric company sends electricity through a wire to your farm and then immediately sends it back through another wire. Then, this is the brilliant part, they send it right back to you again.

This means that an electric company can sell a customer the same batch of electricity thousands of times each day and not get caught, since very few consumers take the time to examine their electricity closely. In fact, the last time any new electricity was generated in the United States was in 1952. The electric companies have been merely reselling it ever since, which is why they have so much free time to apply for rate increases.

Actually, I don't think the electric company has any idea how much electricity I use. You see, for the last eleven years a huge nest of killer wasps has protected my electric meter.

Nobody, not even the dog, goes near that thing. So I am sure that the meter reader just picks out a farm with a barn about the size of mine and uses their reading to make out my bill.

I hope this brief explanation helps you better understand the modern miracle of electricity.

MY NEW SMERFF

In an effort to reduce air pollution, decrease our dependence on Mideast oil, and appear trendy, we at Peckhaven Farm decided to invest in an electric vehicle. Most farms have many far-flung buildings, trenches, hutches, mail boxes, shops and tool sheds that are a fair way apart, so much time is lost daily in just the necessary travel between them. This vehicle will enable us traverse the farmstead for a variety of time consuming tasks that we otherwise have to do on foot.

Some farms have opted for other solutions. For instance, we ruled out the popular 'four wheeler' since there would be too much temptation to see how fast it could go or how easy it would be to make all four wheels leave the ground at once going over a hump in a field or a woodchuck hole, which would surely result in a broken collarbone and a bruised ego. Those opting for strength and speed prefer the ever-popular 'Gator', but again, we don't go for fads.

No, you'll see us putting along toward our greens in our very safe Slow Moving Electric Rural Farm Fetcher, here after referred to as SMERFF. We find it useful to service our calf hutches, get the mail, and hunt for things that have fallen off tractors, such as draw pins, log chains and radiator caps. Yes, it is now par for the course for farmers to enjoy such handy devices.

Our SMERFF has many customized features for farmers. For example, there is a handy little clip on the face of the steering wheel to hold our 'to do' list and two large pockets with straps to hold farm tools on the back as we travel across the farmstead. There are also holders built into the dash of the SMERFF for our water bottles, cans of WD-40, and hornet spray.

Now, I know you golfers with eagle eyes are going to point at my SMERFF and say it looks very familiar. In its defense, let me say that in another life perhaps it made it easier for some mature people with too much leisure time to chase a little white ball around what was once a perfectly good pasture. But please, don't get me tee'd off. Despite all the similarities, it is not a golf cart, it's a SMERFF!

Chapter 7

HOW TO SURVIVE WINTER

The older I get, the harder it is to tolerate the three coldest, snowiest months of the year. The other nine months I try not to think about it. I keep telling myself that fall and spring are wonderfully crisp and refreshing. Of course, summers are always short-sleeve wonders, even when they are too hot or too cold or too wet or too dry.

Winters, on the other hand, require special emphasis on behavior modification. First, I ignore the obvious fact that winter is only 90 days long, for within that period there are several intervals of almost tolerable weather. In most winters the total time of bitter cold or snowstorms is less than 40 days. The lulls give us time to plow snow, thaw pipes and fix manure spreaders. That means we only have to face 50 days of 'tough sledding' before spring arrives.

I also pass the time by telling myself that the deep mud of spring is worse than the ice I just slipped on, spilling all four buckets of milk intended for the calves.

Actually, the best part of winter is the decreased hours of sunlight. In early December it's almost dark by five p.m. What a great excuse to stop work and find things that need doing which can be done sitting down in a warm house. As spring approaches the hours of daylight again lengthen, forcing us to feel guilty inside when we could be working outside. So,

December and January are the times to sort through all the old newspapers you didn't have time to read last May and June, recycle all the outdated catalogs that you have saved, read the instructions for all the computerized gadgets you bought but haven't figured out yet how to use, and actually start reading one of the books in your precariously balanced stack of books in your 'to read someday' pile.

My wife uses these dark winter nights for similarly important tasks. I might come home to find the whole living room rug filled with small piles of bills and receipts she is sorting in preparation for filing income taxes. On those nights I have to hide out in the shop sorting nuts and bolts with my mittens on.

Relish this chance to catch up on these essential tasks because, before you know it, spring will be here and you will be slipping and spilling your calf pails down a muddy slope instead of an icy one.

THE BLIZZARD OF '93

We knew it was coming. The radio touted it as the storm of the century, ominously falling on the thirteenth day of March. With this much warning, I was prepared. Everything was put under cover; chores were done ahead where possible. Yes, I felt ready for the excess of two feet of snow that eventually fell. I even plugged in the heater on one of the diesel tractors, so it would start in the event of power failure.

I had almost finished milking when it happened. It was dramatic. Instantly all the lights went out, the milkers fell off and the electric motors stopped. All that could be heard was the howling of the wind and the groans of some very disappointed cows. Bless the power company, 'specialist in stray voltage for over seventy years'.

Confidently I grabbed a flashlight and started for the tractor shed. It was at this point that I realized the enormity of the situation. While the wind had swept some areas clear, my path was blocked by many waist-high snow drifts that I could only wallow through on my knees. What I needed were snow shoes.

I don't remember what happened to the pair my father had. In the early years of grass silage development he used them to level and pack the fresh direct-cut grass blown into our small upright silo. Suddenly I recalled the time he was patiently explaining how he did this to my nutty Aunt Milly. Her only reaction was, "Boy, I'd have enough trouble climbing up a silo chute without wearing snow shoes, too." Bless his soul, with a straight face, my father replied that no, he didn't climb the ladder wearing snow shoes, but pulled them up with a rope. Then, and only then, did he put them on. Visions of my aunt climbing up a silo chute wearing snow shoes gave me the strength to get to the tractor shed.

Fortunately I got the tractor started and connected to the generator. Within minutes the farm began to hum and glow. I survived the 'blizzard of '93', but I still don't know what happened to my dad's old snowshoes.

CHRISTMAS DAY

Christmas is the time of year when farm families all over the country ask themselves the age old question, "What will go wrong on Christmas day this year?" as it is nothing short of a miracle when the entire farm family can spend Christmas together.

You see, taking care of cows is much like taking care of a baby. You are never done, just caught up for a while. Whether it is the next milking, the next feeding or the next diaper change, it is always something. This adds to the challenge of finding quality time to enjoy holiday traditions, like emptying stockings, tearing open gifts and resetting the Christmas tree, thanks to the cat. Most farm families find Christmas a joyous time of year and would like to spend as much time in the house together on Christmas day as possible.

God understands this basic need, so in his infinite wisdom, each Christmas day God tests our perseverance and ingenuity in new and exciting ways. One year it was a major hip-deep, bone-chilling, eyebrow-frosting, teeth-chattering and feet-freezing snow storm, dragging out even the simplest of chores and forcing snow removal to take precedence over opening presents in a warm house. Some years it is the first below-zero day, resulting in comatose diesel tractors, frozen cattle waterers and numb fingertips.

Other times it is not weather-related at all. So much can go wrong on a modern dairy farm. A delay could be caused by anything from a burned-out electric motor, a cow needing assistance in delivering a large calf, or having to extricate a traveler embedded in a snow bank. Whatever it is, it will make the barn crew the last present to be delivered on Christmas day. You can also be assured that chores will go smoothly on both the day before Christmas and the day after.

CHRISTMAS IN THE ONE-ROOM SCHOOL

"Have you learned your piece yet?" shouted one of my classmates, as we both arrived at the door of our one-room schoolhouse one cold December morning nearly sixty years ago.

While my memories of life in a one-room country school sare still clear to me, the thoughts of the annual Christmas celebration are most vivid. In those years following World War II, the days of the little red schoolhouse were numbered. By then transportation and communications had improved enough to make them obsolete. But to me, those days were the center of my childhood universe.

The annual Christmas festivities included a short play, usually written by the teacher, in which every student had a role. The curtain for the stage was a sheet thrown over a wire strung across the front of the room. We all thought it was more dramatic than a Broadway play. We would have a real Christmas tree, usually cut in the woods nearby by the older boys anxious to have a few hours off during the school day. After presents were exchanged between those whose names had been drawn from a hat, each child received a small box of candy with a flimsy string handle for carrying. Invariably, as we left the building, someone's string handle would break and candy would spill all over the oil-soaked wooden floors.

But what I remember most is the short Christmas poem each student committed to memory and recited for all the parents gathered for the evening's festivities. These poems, or 'pieces', as they were called, were memorized and delivered as rapidly as possible, in order to get them over with before forgetting the words. As a consequence, no thought was given to voice inflection, pacing or dramatic presentation. I will never forget the scene of one little kid after another standing terrified before a captive audience, rattling off their pieces without understanding a word they were saying, before the gaze of their proud parents.

With every speech I give or play I am in, I still mentally reflect on those first attempts at entertaining an audience.

FOOLING THE COWS

Sometimes cows can be just plain finicky. Since they were born with fur coats and insulated leggings, cold weather doesn't seem to bother them. In fact, the colder it is, the more milk they give. I always forget about this bovine proclivity until it turns cold in the fall and the bulk tank readings begin to rise.

While my fingers were freezing during one January morning milking, my mind began to wander. What if I could convince my cows that it was winter all year round? I bet I could increase production per cow without costing me much money.

This might not be as easy as it sounds for cows are not easily fooled. I know because they saw through my last cost-cutting brainstorm of substituting sawdust for grain in their total mixed ration.

Anyway, next spring I plan to institute a few practices to trick my cows into thinking it is winter all year. First, I will pipe Christmas music or the sound of howling wind into the barn several hours a day. That, coupled with a continuous snowfall just outside the rear door of the barn, ought to keep my bovine beauties in the wintertime mood most of the year. I figure that staging a simulated snowfall should be easy using excess Styrofoam peanuts from packing boxes and a strategically placed electric fan.

Our barn has several large fans for keeping the cows cool during the summer. I may have to leave them on all year to prevent the more astute cows from noticing the difference between summer and winter. Drapes could be used to make it darker earlier in the day during the summer months, simulating the dark, dreary days of winter. Since I have an automatic icemaker in my refrigerator, adding ice cubes to the waterers all summer will be the crowning touch.

Between the Christmas music, fake snow, darkened barn, and ice in the drinking water, the cows will never know that it is summer. And better yet, maybe the milk tank will be full! I am surprised that I didn't think of this sooner!

SPRING IS COMING

A farmer's life is one of making weighty decisions and then having to live with the results of those decisions. Take tractor chains, for example. We are pulling our big mixer wagon around our hilly farmstead with a tractor that is really too light and underpowered for the weight it has to pull. This isn't a problem most of the year, but after the first snowfall, the finger-pinching, frustrating and finger-numbing job of putting the chains on the mixer wagon tractor becomes inevitable. Understandably, this action is put off as long as possible. In fact, the final decision to put the chains on usually is made the day the whole outfit jackknives and slides tight against the barn door. Once the chains are installed, with rubber straps keeping them tight, we bounce along all winter with few traction problems.

Because tractor chains are so hard to install, deciding when they are no longer needed is also a major problem. As spring approaches and the snow melts and bare spots begin to appear in the driveway, chains may not be necessary. But there is always the possibility that we could get a substantial snowfall in the middle of April. It is this fear that keeps us slogging through our muddy lanes with the chains clanging away, their sleigh bell-like noise a daily reminder of our lack of confidence.

Also, when you put chains on a tractor you get so accustomed to their superior traction that after a few months it is possible to gradually convince yourself that the tractor would be helpless without them. One year this fear of removing the chains got so out of hand that I found myself doing the spring plowing with the chains still chattering away. Only after my neighbor assured me that a snowstorm after May first was very unlikely did I have courage enough to go chainless.

So this is my dilemma. Should we take the chains off early and risk sliding against the barn again, or leave them on and look and sound stupid? That's the kind of decisions farmers have to make every day. Now, doesn't that make your problems seem insignificant?

THE TWELVE DAYS OF CHRISTMAS ON THE FARM

One of the many reasons I look forward to the holiday season is the opportunity to sing my favorite carol, "The Twelve Days of Christmas". Although my family insists that I am musically impaired, I still love belting out this unusual cumulative English carol. The twelve days of Christmas of course refer to those days between Christmas and Epiphany, not the time it takes to teach a cow to gift wrap.

This traditional carol may have a proud heritage, but it is in dire need of updating. No one in today's modern hip culture would send gifts such as a partridge in a pear tree or ten lords a leaping! Those of us on farms trying to impress our true loves might provide a more appropriate and useful list of gifts, free of feathered creatures like French hens and turtle doves. My version might go something like this:

On the first day of Christmas my true love sent to me
    A tractor with a big cab.
On the second day of Christmas my true love sent to me
    Two bags of milk replacer and a tractor with a big cab.
On the third day of Christmas my true love sent to me
    Three Tingley boots, two bags of milk replacer and a tractor with a big cab.
        (You know how the song goes from here.)
On the fourth day of Christmas my true love sent to me
    Four cows a mooing.

On the fifth day of Christmas my true love sent to me
  Five snow shovels.
On the sixth day of Christmas my true love sent to me
  Six bottles of hand cream.
On the seventh day of Christmas my true love sent to me
  Seven warm meals a-waiting.
On the eighth day of Christmas my true love sent to me
  Eight heifers bagging.
On the ninth day of Christmas my true love sent to me
  Nine breeders breeding.
On the tenth day of Christmas my true love sent to me
  Ten hoof trimmers a-trimming.
On the eleventh day of Christmas my true love sent to me
  Eleven vets a-vetting.
On the twelfth day of Christmas my true love sent to me
        Twelve milk testers testing,
        Eleven vets a-vetting,
        Ten hoof trimmers a-trimming,
        Nine breeders breeding,
        Eight heifers bagging,
        Seven warm meals a-waiting,
        Six bottles of hand cream,
        Five snow shovels,
        Four cows a mooing,
        Three Tingley boots,
        Two bags of milk replacer and
        A tractor with a big cab.

   Now isn't that more appropriate for your favorite farmer
than a whole bunch of drummers drumming and pipers pip-
ing? You bet it is! Merry Christmas!

NUMBERS

I always thought that a thorough understanding of numbers and how they are derived would put me one up on those that don't have such knowledge. At the same time, numbers can be deceiving.

For example, while others were lamenting how wet their fields were this spring, I was comforted by the fact that my farm had received less than an inch of precipitation each time it rained. At last, I thought, I had conquered the cycles of bad weather that have always plagued farmers. Then I discovered that my rain gauge had a hole in it. What a let down. I guess that explains why my fields are as wet as everyone else's.

It was like the winter we didn't have any days when the temperature dropped below zero. Was it too good to be true? For the first time in years no frozen pipes, no comatose tractors and no frozen teat ends. With such seeming good fortune coming my way, I was heartbroken to discover the markings on my porch thermometer had slid too far down to correctly read the temperature. Anyway, that would explain why we had so many days over 100 degrees that summer.

That experience reminded me of my youth. I anxiously measured my height frequently, hoping to be tall enough to try out for the basketball team. One day I was elated to find that I had grown an inch in only two weeks. But alas, my dreams of being a famous athlete were dashed when I realized that some one had broken the first inch off the eight-foot tape I was using.

My life has been full of mishaps with numbers. I thought my pickup was getting over 40 miles per gallon. Then I found the odometer was less than honest in counting the miles traveled. And there was the time my over zealous grain drill gave my fields more acres than they deserved and my increased daily milk production was actually a faulty dipstick on my bulk tank. I have come to distrust any numbers that appear to be in my favor.

I hope we never go to the metric system. I won't know if I am coming or going.

A CHRISTMAS STORY

As the Christmas season approaches, that wondrous time of the year, many rituals will be repeated yet again. The annual newspaper story begging for sympathy for those who must work on Christmas day is one of my favorites.

It never fails. Some cub reporter is asked to write a tear-provoking story reminding us that not everyone has Christmas day off to spend with his or her family. I have come to expect interviews with policemen, firemen and nurses who must provide essential services on this very special family holiday. Never mentioned is the dairy farmer who must feed and care for his cows as well as milk them twice every day, whether it is Christmas or not.

Last year a newspaper story brought tears to my eyes when a pet store manager confessed that he had to leave his family on Christmas day to go in to feed his pets. It took him almost an hour to do this. BIG DEAL! The average dairy farmer spends at least eight hours, maybe ten, every Christmas away from his family just caring for his cows. Don't get me wrong, I am not complaining for this is the life I chose. All dairy farmers ask is a little recognition for their unselfish contribution of providing the American consumer with an endless supply of wholesome dairy products at a reasonable cost.

I believe the real reason farmers are not mentioned in these newspaper stories is that nobody knows that dairy farmers exist. The common belief is that milk and dairy products really come from large refrigerated trucks. Cows have nothing to do with it. They merely while away their days posing for cow posters and butter dish patterns.

COLD SNAP

There was a time when I considered winter as my least favorite season. Summers on the farm are so nice with their warmth, and fall brings crisp cool days, but winter can be very hard to take. However last winter my views changed. Isn't it amazing how Mother Nature keeps tricking us?

November and December were warmer than normal. In fact, the weather remained warm well into the new year. Then, when the cold finally hit, what a shock it was! The temperature fell from a balmy 35 degrees to below zero in less than a day. The weatherman called it an artic air mass. I called it something else.

We suffered through a week of below zero mornings that daily revealed other flaws in our carefully winterized farmstead. For example, we found which heated waterers kept flowing at five degrees above zero but not at five below. We learned which diesel engines required a few more hours of engine heater time and we determined which parts of our complicated water system needed more insulation. And we quickly learned how many layers of clothing we needed to stay warm and keep our fingers from going numb.

After that killer of a week, the rest of the winter was a snap. Temperatures in the ten to twenty degree range seemed downright tropical. Cold mornings were not a problem after what we had been through, because we knew it could be worse. Even though it was hard to get going on a cold winter morning, it was a pleasure because the teat dip no longer froze in the parlor, we didn't have to break the ice on the waterers and we didn't miss watching the cows steamy breath wafting across the feedbunk, as if they were smoking.

It's too bad we couldn't apply this 'trial by fire' principle to other situations as well. Maybe we could stand the hottest summer days if we conditioned ourselves in a sauna first. Perhaps we could take a three-day rain better if we practiced walking through mud a foot deep beforehand. Possibly loading 50-pound bags of grain would be a cinch, if we practiced with a few 100-pound bags first. Maybe next fall I'll sit in a freezer to prepare myself for the coming winter.

The bright spot is that I think I've finally outsmarted Mother Nature. I can handle what ever she might throw at me. Just think, now that I don't have to spend all fall dreading winter, I might just have time to sort my sock drawer after all.

Chapter 8

WHAT DO YOU MAKE?

I am always amazed at the number of people who don't have any idea what farmers do or how important farmers are. Following a discussion of important occupations at a recent dinner party hosted by one of my new neighbors, a successful businessman turned to me and asked, "Joe, What do you make?"

I replied, "You want to know what I make?"

I make enough milk to give four thousand people three glasses of milk a day every day. I make it possible to preserve the land I work for future generations to either grow crops or build houses on. I make the land produce thousands of tons of forage for my cattle and still keep it in better condition than when I assumed responsibility for it over four decades ago. I make my neighborhood a better place to live by keeping my land and buildings neat.

I make my community a priority by reaching out to neighbors and becoming involved in community initiatives. I make sense of the many government programs, surveys and mandates with which I am bombarded. I make a significant contribution to the national and local economy by providing jobs for several valued employees and by purchasing goods and services locally.

I make time to serve on boards and committees and provide leadership where needed to improve our community. I make the prevention of urban sprawl a goal by supporting planning decisions that encourage wise land use. I make real estate taxes increase at a much slower rate by keeping my land in agriculture rather than in intense uses dependent on high public spending.

I make it a priority to leave enough trees and brush surrounding my fields so our precious wildlife will have adequate habitat to thrive. I seek to make my new neighbors happy by providing open space, a bucolic farmstead and active farm operations for them to view as they pass by my farm. I make every effort to prevent my farm operations from becoming an inconvenience and nuisance to my non-farm neighbors.

I make it a point to answer questions or tell anyone who will listen about my farm, its operations and our reasons for doing things the way that we do. I make many lives brighter by writing a monthly humorous column about my life on the farm. I make time for my family a priority, for it's the family involvement that makes farming so unique. I make every attempt to extol the efficiency and productivity of the American farmer, who produces enough to feed ninety-eight people in this country and thirty abroad.

"What do I make? As you can see, I make a difference."

EVENING CHORES

The trouble with milking cows is that it is a job that cannot be hurried. When it is my turn to do the evening milking, I like to start early enough to finish at a decent hour. This is possible if I do all the time-consuming detail jobs first so as not to be stuck with them after the milking is done. Sounds easy, doesn't it?

The problem comes from assuming that everything will go according to plan, as I plod through the repetitive steps of feeding, milking and cleaning up after 100 bosomy bovines. Invariably something happens to disrupt the smooth flow of the milking operation.

I've grown to expect such interruptions as the untimely arrival of a calf, the holding area gate coming unlatched, and a long lost friend popping in, expecting to spend a few hours reminiscing about old times. These obstacles I can handle for they are no worse than a broken pipe or manure splashed in the eye, which are almost daily happenings.

No, the big interruptions I dread are the completely unforeseen events that are topics of conversation for years. My most memorable 'late milking' story actually happened last fall. As I finished all the preparations to start at an unheard of half-hour early I noticed two hot air balloons on the horizon. This mode of transportation has always fascinated me, so I watched as they drew nearer.

Living on a hill has its advantages. It soon was obvious that they were going to land in my big alfalfa field. Already a crowd had gathered along the road. Now everyone knows the wonderful tradition of giving the property owner a bottle of champagne. How could I start milking without going out in my field to collect my prize?

After that, 'late milking' interruptions such as phone calls from friends wanting to borrow something or the bulldozer man wanting me to pull him out of the pond don't seem as exciting as they once did.

PRICELESS

When a farmer makes a decision, the value of the result must always be weighed very carefully. If the wrong decision is made, the cost could be very high. In those rare cases when the right decision is made, the value is truly priceless.

For example, this fall we had the good weather and the good credit to be able to install over 10,000 feet of tile in several fields that often were too wet to till early enough to plant corn or seed in a timely fashion. These wet spots, over the years, have caused a great deal of anguish, broken tow chains and profanity. The tile costs 30 cents a foot plus one dollar a foot to install, but the value of not getting the tractor and manure spreader stuck in the same spot every spring is priceless.

Because we have owned most of our old farm machines for a very long time we have learned which parts wear out most often. Trying to keep a supply of these parts on hand to take care of untimely breakdowns is expensive. We easily have thousands of dollars tied up in spare parts, belts and hoses at any one time to address the most common breakdowns.

Does it pay to have that much money tied up in inventory? Well, one Sunday afternoon a bearing wore out on the outboard end of the pickup head on our self-propelled chopper. We had 20 acres of fourth cutting left to chop. And the day, which had started out clear and dry, now showed a sky filled with ominous grey clouds. By pawing through several boxes of parts marked 'chopper', we found a new bearing that fit. After several skinned knuckles and a few minutes time we were back in business. You might say: value of spare parts $4,000; value of finishing fourth cutting before the rain and before it got too dry: priceless.

Farming through a prolonged period of low prices can be frustrating, testing the management skills, miserliness and bill-shuffling ability of the most patient farmer. Not having enough money to make the capital investments necessary to keep the farm competitive may be a disadvantage, but not having to deal with a procession of salesmen promoting their latest gimmicks because they know you cannot pay for them is really priceless.

It is the same way with cows. When a cow gets sick you have a choice of starting an aggressive course of treatment or giving up and sending the cow for beef before spending a fortune trying to get her well enough to milk again. The cost of treatment including a stomach operation, antibiotics and lost milk might run over $400 but the sight of her standing there bright and alert, chewing her cud and dripping milk: priceless.

On a farm it often seems like everything is going wrong. That's why when things do go right it's priceless.

CHANGE

The buzzword today seems to be 'change'. Personal coaches, management consultants and even young mothers all talk about change. Well, let me tell you, no one has seen as much change as a farmer. No, I don't mean change in his pocket, but change in the way he does things. One inspirational speaker says there are only two kinds of people, those who welcome change and those who don't, but must change anyway. I am not sure where farmers fall, but we seem to be destined to change.

It is hard to believe that for many centuries farming changed very little. Sons could learn the trade from their fathers and pass it along to their sons, with very little change in methods, machinery or business size. Today the science of farming is changing faster than a cow can find a hole in a new fence. In fact, farming has changed so much that it has its own language now, with such unpronounceable words as NYSCHAP, CAFO, and POOP.

We used to sow and reap crops more or less when we got around to it. Now, to determine when to plant and harvest, careful records must be kept of growing degree-days, minimum and maximum air temperatures and when the elm leaves are the size of a squirrel's ear.

That's not all. Feeding cows isn't the same either. For generations cows had to make do with whatever could be grown on the farm. Here is where we see the greatest modification in farming methods. Just to keep our cows full of grub requires a computer-generated feed program, a mixer wagon with electronic scales, a selection of silages, grains and other stuff, and, most of all, someone who can add up a column of figures in their head, while driving a tractor in the rain.

Yes, we may have gone from a scythe to a self-propelled combine to harvest grain, from a three-legged stool to a 12 on-a-side parlor to collect milk, and from a sickle to a whopper chopper to harvest hay, but one thing has not changed – farmers still have to work on the weekend while everyone else is reading up on how to embrace change.

RECYCLED BARNS

It was billed as a tour of studios, galleries and farms. It sounded innocent enough. It would be an opportunity to see how a once thriving agricultural area was changing as more farmers retired and more 'outsiders' moved into the former farms. The tour was an opportunity to show off new uses for once proud dairy barns.

The first stop was a dairy barn turned into a high-class carpentry/cabinetmaker shop. The tie stalls were gone, replaced by plywood floors on which stood a plethora of precise woodworking machines, many of which I had never seen before. We walked past a long beautiful table soon to grace a corporate boardroom. Similar exquisite custom-made cabinets stood in various stages of completion. This barn and this craftsman were turning out many beautiful pieces where a fine herd of registered Ayrshire cattle once stood. I didn't know whether to laugh or cry. I knew the dairyman who owned those cows. I hope he understood that the new caretaker cared for his craft as much as the farmer did for his.

Our next visit was to another former dairy barn, now a beautifully decorated marketplace for floral designs, specialty foods and handicrafts. The hayloft is now full of racks for drying flowers and herbs and the milking parlor is now a workshop for wreath making and craft classes. It is a successful business without a cow anywhere. I was sad to see the empty stanchions but happy to see a new use for such a well built structure.

We sped on to an old hay barn converted to an art gallery for several local artists. Again, I was glad to see a new use for a proud old English-style center drive-through barn. The art was tastefully displayed on the hand hewn beams and rough sawed boards, but missing was the smell and dust of over ripe timothy hay that this barn had stored for over one hundred years. As I looked at those huge beams and carefully fitted joints, I wished that those early carpenters could see this new use for their old barn.

It wasn't until our last stop that we saw a real farm with a large herd of dairy cows milked in a circular parlor. It even had a raised platform so that the entire milking operation could be viewed through a picture window, protecting the viewers from the odors and splash of a usual parlor visit.

I felt right at home. To me that was the best art of all.

HISTORY LESSON

How many cataclysmic movements that ultimately changed history were started by accident? I am talking, of course, about the answer to that age old question, "What would have happened to our farm economy if the free stall had never been invented?"

We all know that in the almost half century since the free stall became the predominate method of housing dairy cattle the milk price has stagnated and the cows per man efficiency factor has quadrupled.

Most people don't realize that prior to the 1960's most dairy cattle were housed in conventional stables where cows were housed, fed and milked in individual stalls that required both individual attention and hours of backbreaking work.

And then it happened! A farmer was in the middle of remodeling his cow barn and left a space in the construction that was long enough for a cow to lay down in and narrow enough so she couldn't turn around in it. When he found this cow laying in the space comfortably chewing her cud, the proverbial light bulb lit up in his head and he asked himself, "What if the cows were able to walk around freely, eat whenever they were hungry and lie in a stall whenever they wanted?"

The rest is history. Large numbers of dairy cows can now be fed and housed with a minimum of labor per cow, thanks to the perfection of the free stall concept and the mixer wagon.

What if that first cow had walked by the free stall space and laid in the alley like most cows do? What if the free stall had not been invented? Would the number of cows per farm be limited? Would the price of milk be higher, both for the farmer and for the consumer? Would the sales of insulated coveralls suffer? Interesting to contemplate, but only for academic reasons because free stalls are here to stay.

IT COULD HAPPEN TO ANYBODY

As I get older and my peripheral vision begins to recede, more unfortunate things seem to happen to me. Take for example, the now famous gate latch incident. We feed our cows by backing an immense mixer wagon through a very narrow rear door of our free stall barn. Most of the time I can do this without mishap. Once I didn't. I happened to lightly touch the self-closing spring-loaded gate latch with the six-ton mixer wagon, bending the latch beyond recognition. Luckily, the mixer wagon was unhurt, but the cows got out and trampled the garden.

I don't look upon minor incidents as being my fault; rather, as things that would have happened anyway and I was just the unlucky person who was driving the tractor at the time they happened. This philosophy has made my life much happier. Like the time I almost tore the muffler off a tractor by catching it on a shade cloth guy wire. It could have happened to anybody who didn't have sense enough to look up as well as sideways before backing up.

Fortunately, not much has happened lately, other than breaking a post off in the heifer barn when it jumped in front of me as I was operating the skid steer, and ripping the lights off a tractor while trying to go under a limb instead of around it. These things used to upset me, but not anymore.

Still, there is nothing that can dampen one's spirits faster than hearing the sound of wood splintering, welds breaking or glass shattering when maneuvering a large farm machine in a tight space. I have learned, after assessing the damage, that I have three choices. I can admit I did it, plead ignorance and wonder with everyone else how it happened, or I can ignore it and hope no one notices. With a flat tire or broken windshield the last option is very difficult to pull off. All I know for sure is that no matter what happens around here, "It could have happened to anybody!"

STAGES OF LIFE

During our lifetime we all go through different stages because our life experiences color our thinking. These stages are particularly easy to recognize in farmers.

I prefer to think of the early years as the curious stage. There is so much to learn, so many questions to be answered. Ideally we should stay in this stage forever. Our modern lives are so complex that we sometimes feel we can't learn it all. Farmers must never lose this desire to learn more about everything that surrounds them.

Unfortunately, some fall victim to the arrogant stage, where they actually think they know it all. This is characterized by a condescending disdain for others who don't share their superior wisdom. People in this stage should be pitied for when they are proven wrong, it's not a pretty sight.

For most of us curious types, the next step is the philosophical stage when life begins to be understandable. We know by now that although things don't always go the way we planned, life will go on anyway. It's more of a "so what if the hay gets wet" kind of philosophy rather than a "OH, NO, the hay is going to get wet" attitude. Too much philosophy and not enough concern can be a disadvantage, though.

The next stage is acceptance. That's when you realize that you will never be rich, famous, or president of the United States. Early in life anything is possible; later reality sets in.

There is a school of thought that most great things are accomplished by those in the young, curious stage when they haven't learned that what they want to do is impossible, as us older folks have.

A good example of this is the challenge many younger dairy farmers have accepted of managing larger herds that require emptying huge manure storages, planting large acreages of corn and harvesting the entire crop of first cutting of hay, all within thirty days. That's a mind-boggling responsibility for us in the philosophical stage. Fortunately the young and curious seem to pull it off every year. I prefer the acceptance stage. It is much easier.

The last phase is the nostalgia phase. That's the easiest and cheapest. All that is required is to constantly remind everyone of how things used to be. This stage is characterized by lengthy descriptions of people, buildings and machines, all long gone. The best part of the nostalgic phase is that you don't have to be terribly accurate about any of the details because as time passes there are fewer and fewer people left who can prove you wrong.

All of these stages are perfectly respectable. However sometimes we are so busy that we don't realize we are in a stage at all.

What stage are you in?

IF ONLY I HAD TIME

Time, they say, is the only thing the rich and poor have in the same amount. How people use their time determines how much of their lives they can be proud of. The cows, alas, take too much of a farmer's time to feed, clean and milk. And even when he's not in the barn, the farmer is guiltily worrying about his cows.

So much time is spent caring for the cows that I often dream about all the things I would like to do but never have the time to do. If only I had time, I would watch a falling star, write a book and wash the car. I would go for mountain hikes, bake breads and cakes and ride my bike, if only I had time.

But there's always a cow to milk, calf to pull, or corn to chop. Otherwise, I could ride the surf, play with a Smerff, or sleep in a berth. I often wonder what it would be like to take a long journey, walk along a beach, or be kind to an attorney. Oh, if only I had the time.

Don't get me wrong. I really do like the cows. If only it didn't take so long to tend to them. They just don't let me have any time to watch a race, weed a garden or steal a base. As I watch those without cows sailing boats, making root beer floats or spouting anecdotes, I can't help but think, if only I had time.

On the other hand, for those too closely tied to the cows, it's almost as much fun dreaming about what you would do, if only you had the time, than it is to actually have the time. Besides, just saying, "I haven't got time" often saves you from visiting relatives, mowing lawns and shopping for laxatives.

So, sometimes, it's not so bad to lament, "If only I had the time".

THE EARTH IS SHRINKING

I am not sure, but I think that the earth is shrinking. I know it is hard to believe that something as obvious as this could occur. Yet, I can find no other explanation for what has happened on our farm in the last half century.

You see, I was born and raised on this farm. As a child its yard, buildings and sprawling fields and pastures were my playground. I knew every inch of it, from the cavernous haymow in the barn to the deep ravines cutting through the fields.

But something has changed. Gradually everything seems to have shrunk. Take the big pasture adjacent to the barn where, as a ten year old, I spent endless hours searching for lost cows, only to find them hidden under a thorn apple tree or nestled in a thicket of elderberry bushes, cuddled up beside a newborn calf. I mean this field was huge, full of steep hills, boggy swamps and areas of dense brush. Over the years it has been cleared, drained, and converted into rotated cropland. Walking across it now takes only a few minutes; driving a tractor from one edge to the other takes just a few seconds. So where did all that land go?

The same thing happened to the big barn. When I was a kid it was topped by an immense open haymow, crossed occasionally by wide hand-hewn beams ideal for simulated tight wire walking. When I climb up there now, it is not nearly as vast. The bents, or spaces between the cross beams, are not nearly as wide as they once were, and the roof isn't as high as it seemed in my childhood. How could a barn shrink?

Maybe I shouldn't be too upset, for as I get older (oops, I mean more mature), the hills are beginning to get steeper, the ravines deeper and the haymow ladder taller. In reality, the only thing that has gotten bigger on our farm is the tax bill.

Maybe the earth isn't shrinking after all. Perhaps it is just that my clothes are shrinking.

THIS IS WHERE I CAME IN

In the good old days, the decade following the end of World War II that is, our whole family would occasionally splurge and go to the movies. The local movie theatre featured only one movie at a time and rarely for more than a few days. All shows were twice a night at 7 and 9. Since we could never finish chores, eat supper and get cleaned up to be there by 7, we always walked in during the movie. We had to wait through the intermission to see the first half of the movie. We all sat there until everything on the screen looked familiar and then we knew, "This is where we came in."

That's the way I feel when someone comes up with a great new innovation for the way we farm. Take pasturing cows for example. Dairy farmers have always let their cows roam their fenced fields harvesting their own forage. Always, that is, until someone found that they could feed from storage year round and keep more cows better fed on less land. This meant, of course, more storage structures and more harvesting and feeding equipment. Now a "new" trend is sweeping across dairy country. It simply says that it is cheaper and easier to let cows harvest their own forage by having them 'graze' in fenced fields. I think this is where I came in.

Another great innovation in feeding dairy cattle was the introduction of alfalfa into what was an all grass diet. Alfalfa, a legume, is able to take nitrogen from the air to produce an abundant high-protein forage. True, alfalfa must be reseeded often and requires the addition of lime to our acid soils, both costly. But, for the last half-century, most farmers thought these limitations well worth it. Now some 'experts' are touting the advantages of all grasses for hay crops. They say grass seedings last much longer, grow on wet soils and produce high quality feed if cut early and often. That sounds great, but if grass hay crops are only good when cut early, most fields are too wet to cut early. That's why growing alfalfa was so readily adopted. It could be cut later and produce more. I think this is where I came in.

From now on, when someone has a great new idea on how I should farm, I am going to study it very carefully, looking for the part that looks familiar, because that is where I came in.

A CHRISTMAS TO REMEMBER

I knew it was going to be a memorable Christmas when I saw the turkey hit the ceiling. But then celebrating Christmas on our farm is always exciting and different.

While most families save the entire day for time together sharing, eating and celebrating, dairy farmers have to sandwich family time in between their daily milking, feeding and cleaning chores. Usually everyone pitches in to get those routine chores out of the way as quickly as possible.

The pies were in the oven and the turkey was sitting on the kitchen counter, ready to be sliced. The dining room table was set with Mom's best china. She was so pleased to have everyone home for Christmas dinner. Our family, at Mom's insistence, enjoys a big Christmas dinner before opening our presents. That way Mom is not working in the kitchen while everyone else is exchanging gifts in the living room.

Most of the barn chores were finished. All that remained was to fill the gas tank on the tractor we use to scrape the freestall barn. Running out of gas on Christmas night would not be a pleasant experience. The old tractor had no brakes, but the barn floor was level so to stop the tractor we just lowered the back blade that acted as an anchor. It always stopped the tractor.

Grandpa was busy studying the chart on how to carve a turkey and contemplating which knife to use for the job. We only had turkey twice a year, so he had never perfected the fine art of carving one. He was so slow that finally Mom snatched the platter from his hands and plopped it right in the middle of our big dining room table, muttering, "Where is everybody? Everything is going to get cold."

I finished refueling the tractor and hurried back to the warm, cozy house. In my haste I did not put a block in front of the tractor tire when I stopped by the gas pump, nor did I let the blade down to act as a brake. This turned out to be a monumental mistake because the tractor, back blade and all, began to roll. We always thought having the barn up hill from the house was an advantage, but it sure wasn't that day. Even as the tractor began to gain speed I wasn't worried. Tractors are heavy and usually roll hard, especially on the uneven and rutted surface of our driveway. I thought it would eventually stop and I could hop aboard, drive it into the barn, close all the gates and go eat dinner.

I guess it wasn't meant to be, for the old, manure-spattered tractor kept bouncing along toward the house, picking up speed with every fence rail it crashed through.

Mom had the potatoes mashed and the sweet potatoes carefully spooned into her favorite serving dish. Everything was nearly ready, if only the barn crew would make their appearance and get cleaned up.

For a while it looked like the tractor would miss the house and plow right into the front of Aunt Milly's new car, but when the tractor ran over a snow-covered lawn chair, the front wheels turned slightly and headed right for the dining room window.

Everyone was busy bringing things to the table. Aunt Milly brought her famous cinnamon swirl rolls, Sharon made her favorite scalloped oyster recipe and Debbie was just putting a dish of pickled beets on the table when it hit. No one heard it coming because the engine wasn't running. Fortunately, the sound of splintering wood and breaking glass caused everyone to step back and clear a path for the tractor. It wouldn't have been so bad if the table hadn't been so close to the window. As the table rose propelled from beneath by a tractor hood, the succulent half-sliced turkey shot skyward, hit the ceiling, hung there for a moment, and fell onto the tractor seat with a sound not unlike that of a football landing in a huge bowl of chocolate pudding.

After we pulled the tractor out of the house and nailed plywood over the gaping hole, everyone feasted on pancakes and canned peaches in the living room before we opened our presents. It was a Christmas to remember!

Order Form

Peckhaven Publishing
178 Wagman's Ridge
Saratoga Springs NY 12866-6620
518 584-4129   FAX 518 226-0096
joe@joepeckonline.com

I wish to order: <u>Quantity</u>

A Tractor In The House & Other Smashing Farm Stories _____
A Cow in the Pool & Udder Humorous Farm Stories _____
Laugh 'Til the Cows Come Home CD _____
The Udder Side of the Story CD _____

Name: _____

Address: _____

City: _____ State _____ Zip _____

<u>Price:</u> **Books $14.95 each**   **Total Books $**_____
      CDs $10.00 each   **Total CDs $**_____
<u>Sales Tax</u>: NYS orders please   **Sales Tax $**_____
include 7% sales tax.
<u>Shipping/Handling</u>:   **Shipping $**_____
$4.00 for the first book,
$2.00 for each additional book
$2.00 for each CD

Total amount enclosed $_____

Please remit in check or money order, payable to:
Peckhaven Publishing

Order Form

Peckhaven Publishing
178 Wagman's Ridge
Saratoga Springs NY 12866-6620
518 584-4129   FAX 518 226-0096
joe@joepeckonline.com

I wish to order: <u>Quantity</u>

A Tractor In The House & Other Smashing Farm Stories _____
A Cow in the Pool & Udder Humorous Farm Stories _____
Laugh 'Til the Cows Come Home CD _____
The Udder Side of the Story CD _____

Name: _____

Address: _____

City: _____ State _____ Zip _____

<u>Price:</u> **Books $14.95 each**   **Total Books $**_____
          CDs $10.00 each   **Total CDs $**_____
<u>Sales Tax:</u> NYS orders please   **Sales Tax $**_____
  include 7% sales tax.
<u>Shipping/Handling:</u>   **Shipping $**_____
  $4.00 for the first book,
  $2.00 for each additional book
  $2.00 for each CD
                    <u>**Total amount enclosed**</u> $_____

Please remit in check or money order, payable to:
Peckhaven Publishing